MYTHS, MURDERS AND MYSTERIES

A NEW WINDMILL BOOK
OF STORIES FROM MANY GENRES

EDITED BY LOUISE NAYLOR

Heinemann
New Windmills

Heinemann Educational Publishers
Halley Court, Jordan Hill, Oxford OX2 8EJ
A division of Reed Educational and Professional Publishing Ltd

OXFORD MELBOURNE AUCKLAND
JOHANNESBURG BLANTYRE GABORONE
IBADAN PORTSMOUTH (NH) USA CHICAGO

03 02 01 00
10 9 8 7 6 5 4

ISBN 0 435 13041 2

Acknowledgements

The Author and Publishers should like to thank the following for permission
to use copyright material:

Dorling Kindersley Children's Books for 'Izanami and Izanagi' from *The Illustrated Book of
Myths* retold by Neil Philip, published by Dorling Kindersley, p6; The Maggie Noach Literary
Agency for 'Pandora's Box' and 'Pyramus and Thisbe' from *Myths and Legends retold by
Anthony Horowitz* published by Kingfisher 1985, copyright © Anthony Horowitz 1985, pp8, 16;
David Higham Associates Ltd for 'A Night at a Cottage' by Richard Hughes from *A Moment of
Time* © Richard Hughes, p26; A. M. Heath & Company Ltd for 'Who Goes Down This Dark
Road?' by Joan Aiken from *A Touch of Chill* published by Gollancz, © 1979 Joan Aiken
Enterprises Ltd, p30; Kingfisher Publications Plc for 'Feeding the Dog' by Susan Price from
Horror Stories chosen by Susan Price published by Kingfisher, copyright © Kingfisher
Publications Plc 1995. All rights reserved, p38; Jennifer Luithlen Agency for 'A Gnaw of Rats'
copyright © 1982 Robert Swindells. First published in *The Wheaton Book of Science Fiction*,
p74; David Higham Associates Ltd for 'Compassion Circuit' by John Wyndham from *The Seeds of
Time* published by Michael Joseph, copyright © John Wyndham 1956, p91; A. P. Watt Ltd and the
Literary Executors of the Estate of H. G. Wells for 'The Stolen Bacillus', p104; David Higham
Associates Ltd for 'The Hitch-hiker' by Roald Dahl from *Eight Further Tales of the Unexpected*
published by Michael Joseph, p118; Carol Silcock for 'Carousel' first published in this volume,
copyright © Carol Silcock 1999, p133; David Higham Associates Ltd for 'The Case for the
Defence' by Graham Greene from *Twenty-one Stories* published by Penguin, p147.

The Publishers have made every effort to trace the copyright holders, but if they have
inadvertently overlooked any, they will be pleased to make the necessary arrangements
at the first opportunity.

Cover design by The Point
Cover illustration by Jerry Hoare
Typeset by Tek-Art, Croydon, Surrey
Printed and bound in the United Kingdom by Clays Ltd, St Ives plc

Contents

Introduction

'Genre' is a French word used to refer to different types of literary form, such as tragedy, comedy, lyric, novel – or short story. The short story is possibly one of the oldest of these genres and is found in almost all cultures; originally made to be listened to rather than read, it survived through constant telling and retelling (often changing in the process) long before the development of written language. The myths in the first section of this book are stories which originated in this way.

Nowadays we tend to think of genre as a way of distinguishing between different types of novel or short story – horror, crime, ghost, mystery, suspense, love and so on. Each of these sub-genres tends to have recognizable features which we may come to expect, for example a particular type of character, plot, tone or language. The author can, of course, choose either to surprise readers or fulfil their expectations! The stories included here are intended both to be read with enjoyment and to introduce Key Stage 3 students to the study of genre in the short story.

This collection contains sixteen entertaining stories from four different genres: Myth, Ghost and Horror, Science Fiction, and Crime and Mystery. It includes both pre-twentieth century and contemporary stories, grouped according to type. Each group provides:

- an introduction to the genre
- stories exemplifying different aspects of the genre, arranged so that they become progressively more challenging
- Reading and Original Writing assignments.

Section 1
Myths

Myths are traditional stories, mostly about gods, kings and heroes. They were passed down by word of mouth sometimes over thousands of years, and were often altered as they were retold.

People have always tried to understand how the world began, the environment they live in and also mankind itself. Many myths try to explain the world creatively, introducing magic or imaginary creatures, such as gods or giants. Good usually wins over bad, but a dangerous creature or an evil spirit may be included to explain the negative aspects of life on earth, such as storms, floods or death.

Other myths try to explain human behaviour and emotions and to provide moral lessons about how we live. As these are experiences common to all people, many myths from around the world are very similar, even though they reflect their own countries and cultures. It is interesting to compare myths from different cultures and to see the similarities in their explanations.

In this collection, a Creation story from Japan accompanies retellings of the Greek myths of Persephone and Pandora's Box, which give one culture's explanation of the existence of the seasons and of evil in the world.

Finally, the tragic Babylonian tale of Pyramus and Thisbe explores the themes of love and hate and examines human emotion and feeling.

How Winter Came to the Earth
Retold by Jacynth Hope-Simpson

A very long time ago, it was always spring and summer.
The flowers bloomed all the time, and the leaves never
withered and died. The same trees would bear flowers
and fruit at the same time. If you wanted to eat, you just
plucked some fruit off the tree, and soon more fruit
would ripen to take its place. The meadows were always
golden and rich with corn. As soon as the reapers cut it
down with their sickles, tender new shoots would begin
to appear through the earth. The goddess of the spring
and summer and harvest was called Demeter. She had
golden hair, the colour of corn when the sun shines on it,
and she was always as peaceful and calm as a long summer's
afternoon. She had one daughter called Persephone,
whom she loved more than anything else in the world.

One afternoon, Persephone and her friends were
picking flowers at a place called Enna in the island of
Sicily. They were in the shade of a wood, for the sun was
only just past its highest. The sound of a little waterfall,
gently splashing, made the air seem cool and fresh.
Persephone was picking the white lilies which grew there
all the year round. She was so anxious to pick more
flowers than any of her friends, that, when her basket
was full, she began to put the flowers in the front of her
dress. Then she spotted a place where the lilies seemed
to grow more thickly than anywhere else. She wandered
a little away from her friends. She had no idea that she
was being watched.

As she moved away from her friends, the man who was
watching her followed. He drove his chariot cautiously,
half-hidden by the shade of the trees. It was Hades, king

of the Underworld. He had seen Persephone in the distance and fallen in love with her. Suddenly, he lashed his horses on and drove swiftly towards her. She spun round to see what the noise was. As she did so, he leapt over the edge of his chariot and dragged her into it. Her dress was torn and the flowers fell out. Despite the plight she was in, she cried out at losing them. She was so used to being treated kindly that at first it never occurred to her that he meant to steal her away.

He urged his horses on. He called on each one by name, and shook the dark reins that lay on their necks. The chariot sped away from the cool, sweet-smelling woods, into a rocky land, where boiling water bubbled up from the earth and the pools reeked of sulphur. Persephone shrieked for her friends and her mother, but mostly for her mother. Suddenly Hades **smote** the earth and a deep gash appeared. The chariot rushed down it, towards the hidden Underworld, where Hades was king.

When Demeter heard that her daughter had disappeared, she swore that she would travel over the whole world to find her, and that she would never rest. She cut two branches of pine and carried them up to the crater of the volcano, Etna. There she lit them, so that their flame would show her the way on her journey. She walked all day, and all night, and all the next night as well. Nobody would have recognized her. Her golden hair, which had been so shining and smooth, now hung lankly over her face, because she had torn at it in her grief. Her eyes, which had been so joyful and calm, were wild. She stopped at a little hut for a drink, and an old woman gave her some barley water. A boy, who was watching her, mocked her, because she looked nearly insane. She threw

---

smote: struck

the dregs of her drink at him, and he turned into a lizard. She wept and was astonished at what she had done.

It would take too long to tell about everywhere that she went to look for her daughter. She did not stop until there was nowhere left in the whole world. Then, at last, she came back to Sicily. There she found Persephone's girdle still floating on a pool, near where she had disappeared into the earth. At the sight of it, Demeter became as wild with grief as if she had only just learnt that her daughter had disappeared. She began to curse the whole of the world, and especially Sicily. She snatched up the farmers' ploughs and smashed them. She laid fierce curses on the land. Now the crops died as soon as they pushed through the earth. If they survived, the heat shrivelled them up, or the cold wind blasted them, or floods washed them away. Birds swooped down and ate up the seeds, as the farmer was scattering them. Weeds choked all the flowers.

Then the fountain-nymph, Arethusa, said, 'Demeter, be merciful to the land. I can tell you where Persephone is. I saw her with my own eyes, as I was gliding along the underground river, Styx. She has become the queen of the Underworld. She looked very sad, but she had the air of a queen.'

When Demeter heard this, she grew frenzied with grief again. When at last she became more calm, she decided to go to heaven to see Zeus, the greatest of all the gods. She implored him to help her, and Zeus at last agreed.

'You can have Persephone back on one condition,' he said. 'If she has let any food pass her lips while she was in the Underworld, she will have to stay there forever.'

Now, Persephone had been so sad in the Underworld that she had never eaten. Hades had tried to tempt her with fine and elaborate food, but she had always pushed it away. Then, one day, she had walked under a pomegranate tree. She had seen the fruit hanging down like little red lanterns. It had reminded her of the happy times when she had gathered the ripe harvest on earth, and so she had picked one pomegranate. She had peeled off the thick skin and chewed at the seeds, which are the edible part of this fruit. She had eaten seven. Nobody would have seen her, if a boy called Ascalaphus, who was working in the garden, had not been spying on her.

Hades said he would let Persephone go, as he believed she had never eaten anything in his kingdom. But, just as she was going, Ascalaphus told him that he had seen Persephone eat the seeds. It seemed now as if she would never escape.

Then Zeus decided to pity the sorrowing mother and child. He could not release Persephone from the world underground forever, because he now knew she had eaten while she was there. So he said that she might go back to her mother for half of the year. The rest of the time, she must stay with Hades.

That is why, every spring, Persephone returns to her mother, Demeter. They laugh and rejoice. The sun shines, the flowers unfold, new-born lambs prance in the fields. Then the corn ripens, and the apples start to go red on the trees. The air is still, and noisy with humming insects. But once high summer is past, autumn draws near, and soon Persephone must go back to her underground kingdom. When she goes, the leaves fall from the trees, mist creeps up from the river valleys and low clouds rest on the mountains. The plants shrivel with cold, and men hunch their shoulders as they walk. Winter has come to the earth, to grip it cruelly, until Persephone comes again in the spring.

Izanami and Izanagi

A Japanese Creation Myth retold by N. Philip

In the beginning, heaven and earth were not divided. Then, from the ocean of chaos, arose a reed, and that was the eternal land ruler, Kunitokotatchi.

Then came the female god, Izanami, and the male, Izanagi. They stood on the floating bridge of heaven and stirred the ocean with a jewelled spear until it curdled, and so created the first island, Onokoro. They built a house on this island, with a central stone pillar that is the backbone of the world. Izanami walked one way around the pillar, and Izanagi walked the other. When they met face to face, they united in marriage.

Their first child was named Hiruko, but he did not thrive, so when he was three, they placed him in a reed boat and set him adrift; he became Ebisu, god of fishermen.

Then Izanami gave birth to the eight islands of Japan.

And finally Izanami began to give birth to the gods who would fashion and rule the world – gods of the sea and gods of the land, gods of wind and rain. But when Izanami gave birth to the god of fire, she was so badly burned that she died.

Izanagi was furious with the fire god and cut him into three pieces. Then he set out to search for Izanami. He went right down into the Land of Gloom looking for her. He called her, saying, 'Come back, my love. The lands we are making are not yet finished!'

She came to him, saying, 'You are too late. I have already eaten the food of this land. But I would like to return. Wait here for me, and I will ask permission from the spirits of the underworld. But do not try to look at me.'

At length, Izanagi got tired of waiting, so he broke off a tooth from the comb he wore in his hair to use as a torch and followed her. When he found her, he saw that she was already rotting, and maggots were swarming over her body. She was giving birth to the eight gods of thunder.

Izanagi drew back, revolted. Izanami called after him, 'Shame on you.' She commanded the foul spirits of the underworld to slay him.

The spirits pursued Izanagi, but he managed to escape. He threw down his headdress and it turned into grapes, which the spirits stopped to eat. Then he threw down his comb, which turned into bamboo shoots, and once again the spirits stopped to eat.

By the time Izanagi reached the pass between the land of the dead and the land of the living, Izanami herself had nearly caught up with him. But Izanagi saw her coming and quickly blocked the pass with a huge boulder that it would take a thousand men to lift, so making a permanent barrier between life and death.

Standing on the other side of the boulder, Izanami shouted, 'Every day I will kill a thousand people, and bring them to this land!'

Izanagi replied, 'Every day I will cause one thousand five hundred babies to be born.'

Then Izanagi left Izanami to rule the Land of Gloom, and returned to the land of the living.

Izanagi came to a grove of orange trees on a plain covered with bush clover. There he bathed at the mouth of a clear stream and, as he washed the filth of the underworld from his face, more gods were born. He wiped his left eye, and created Amaterasu, goddess of the sun. He wiped his right eye, and created Tsuki-yomi, god of the moon. He wiped his nose, and created Susanowo, god of the tempest.

Pandora's Box
Retold by Anthony Horowitz

There are some who say that the original creator of mankind was Prometheus, that he fashioned the first man in the image of the gods using clay and water taken from Panopeus in Phocis. Prometheus was a Titan, one of the race of giants who fought an unsuccessful war against Zeus and the other gods – and it is certainly true that he was a great deal wiser than his brothers.

For he alone knew that the war was doomed to failure. He realized that, huge and immensely strong though the Titans undoubtedly were, they also suffered from a common **trait** amongst giants. They just weren't very bright. A Titan might tear up a mountain instead of going round it, but he would probably find out later on that he was going the wrong way anyway. A Titan might be able to hurl a rock the size of Gibraltar a hundred miles or more, but he would invariably miss whatever he was aiming for.

On the other hand, of course, the gods were as quick-witted as they were skilled in the art of war. First there was Zeus, the king of Olympus, armed with his devastating thunderbolts. Then there was Poseidon with his trident, Apollo with his golden arrows, the invisible Hermes . . . it was an **invincible** army and Prometheus could see that his brothers would be lost against it.

Lose was what they did. Most of them were sent to a dark and damp prison in the depths of Tartarus. Atlas – perhaps the most famous Titan of all – was condemned to

---

trait: characteristic
invincible: unbeatable

hold up the heavens on his shoulders for all time. But Prometheus, who had let every one know that he was neutral from the start, got away scot free. That was when he created man.

Prometheus loved men in the same way people love their pets. He was immensely proud of everything they did, boasted about them to almost anyone who would listen, and generally fussed over them in every way possible. Instead of feeding them with food, however, he fed them knowledge – scraps of information that he picked up from Athene, the goddess of wisdom and his only real friend in Olympus. One day she would tell him about mathematics and straight away he would rush down to earth to pass it on. The next day it might be art or architecture, the day after that science or engineering. It's strange to think that our entire civilization could have been handed down to us rather in the manner of dog biscuits, but that is how it was.

As the years passed and mankind became more intelligent, Zeus, who had been watching all this from his **celestial** throne, grew uneasy.

'I am a little worried about these human beings,' he remarked to his wife, Hera, one day over a goblet of wine.

'What about them?' Hera asked.

'Well . . . I just wonder if they're not getting a bit . . . above themselves. Where will it all lead to? That's what I want to know. Today the rudiments of geometry, tomorrow it could be genetic surgery.'

'So what are you going to do about it?'

'I don't know. But I'm keeping my eye on them!'

Zeus might have been a jealous god, but he was not cruel enough to destroy the newly formed human race. And so mankind continued to flourish. Things came to a

---

celestial: heavenly

head, however, one day in a place called Sicyon. The trouble was caused by a question of ownership.

Prometheus had taught man to stay on the right side of the gods by regularly sacrificing the best animals from their herds. A special sacrificial bull had been chosen for Zeus at Sicyon, but the question was, which part should be reserved for the god and which parts should the men (who had worked hard to raise the animal in the first place) be allowed to keep? As usual, Prometheus acted as the mediator in the dispute but, unwisely, he decided to play a trick on Zeus.

When the bull had been killed and cut up, he took two sacks. Into one of these, he put all the most succulent portions of meat – the rump and the fillet, the sirloin and the rib – but concealed them beneath the stomach-bag which was all white and rubbery and generally disgusting to look at. Into the other went the bones and the gristle, the eyeballs and the hooves . . . in short all the most unappetizing parts of the bull. But these were covered with a layer of fat to make them look as delicious as possible.

Then Prometheus took both sacks and knelt before Zeus.

'Oh mighty king!' he said. 'Why should there be any quarrel between you and the little pink creatures who inhabit the world below? Take this matter of sacrifice. It seems that nobody can decide who should get exactly what. Well, as you are the king of Olympus, why don't you choose for yourself? I have divided the bull between these two sacks. Which one do you want?'

Zeus, who had never suspected that a Titan could think up such a scheme, was completely deceived. He chose the bones and the fat and ever since that time the gods have received nothing else from the sacrifice. When he found out how Prometheus had tricked him, however, he was furious.

'Man may have his steak,' he thundered. 'But he will eat it raw!'

And with those words, he reached out with one hand and snatched all the fire from the world.

It seemed that mankind had got the worst deal after all. Without fire they could take no pleasure in their food and once the sun had gone down, they could only stay indoors, huddled under animal skins for warmth. But Prometheus was willing to do anything to help his creation and one day, while Zeus was out having one of his many affairs, he stole up to Olympus. For he still had one friend in the home of the gods: Athene. Hearing him knocking on a side-door, the goddess of wisdom unbolted it and let him in. Then Prometheus rode up to the sun and, using his bare hands, broke off a blazing fire-brand. This he carried back to earth, thrusting it into a giant fennel-leaf. And in this way people were once again able to enjoy their meat *grillé*.

But this time Prometheus had gone too far. When Zeus heard how he had been defied for a second time, his anger knew no bounds.

'Prometheus!' he cried. 'You crossed me once and I forgave you because of your loyalty to me in the war of the Titans. But this time there can be no forgiveness. This time you must pay for your crime.'

And so saying, he seized Prometheus and chained him to a pillar on the freezing slopes of the Caucasian mountains. But if this was not punishment enough, worse was to come. Every morning a huge vulture landed on the wretched Titan's chest and even as he screamed in rage and horror, tore out his liver and devoured it. And every night, while Prometheus shivered in the sub-zero temperatures, his liver grew whole again. In this way the horrible torture could be repeated again and again until the end of time.

Zeus punished mankind too. But as man had only offended indirectly, his punishment was of another sort.

First he visited the crippled god Hephaestus who worked at a great forge in Olympus with twenty bellows pumping twenty-four hours a day. Although ugly and misshapen himself, no blacksmith was more skilled than Hephaestus.

'I want you to make me a woman,' the king of the gods commanded. 'I want her to be more beautiful than any woman ever seen on the face of the earth. She must be perfect. As perfect as a goddess.'

Hephaestus did as he was told. He had only ever disobeyed Zeus once. That had been just before he became the crippled god. Now he fashioned a woman out of clay, moulding her perfect features with his own hands. He commissioned the four winds to breathe life into her and asked all the goddesses to help dress her in their finest clothes and jewels.

The result was Pandora.

When Zeus saw the blacksmith-god's work he was well pleased and instructed Hermes to carry her into the world at once. There she was married to a certain King Epimetheus, the brother of Prometheus and the only other Titan who had not joined in the war against the gods.

Now Epimetheus had been warned never to trust the gifts of Zeus, but seeing the terrible fate that had befallen his brother, he was too afraid to refuse. Moreover, he had to admit that Pandora was beautiful. You'd have had to be mad to think otherwise. When she walked into the room, men fell silent and all eyes turned on her. Whatever she said, people would agree. When she made jokes, the laughter would continue for several minutes. Whatever she did was greeted with applause. And Epimetheus did feel rather proud to be married to her.

Unfortunately, the things Pandora said were never really worth listening to, for she was not a very intelligent creature. Her jokes were in truth extremely unfunny. She did very little because she was impossibly lazy and if Epimetheus was glad to be her husband, she made him a poor and unfaithful wife. For this was the revenge of Zeus. He had made her as shallow and as coquettish as she was beautiful. And she was to cause more trouble to mankind than any woman before or any woman since.

For Epimetheus owned a large ebony box which was kept in a special room in his palace, guarded day and night. In this box he had collected and imprisoned all the things that could harm mankind. It was the one room in the palace that Pandora was forbidden to enter and naturally it was the one room that most aroused her curiosity.

'I bet you keep all sorts of super things in that big, black box of yours,' she would say in her syrupy voice. 'Why don't you let your little Pandy look inside?'

'It is not for you, my dear,' Epimetheus would reply. 'You should leave well alone.'

'But . . .'

'No, no, my love. No one may open the box.'

'Then you don't love me,' Pandora would say, crossing her arms and pouting. 'And I'm not going to love you any more – not ever!'

They had this conversation many times until the day when Pandora couldn't resist her curiosity any longer. For despite everything Epimetheus had told her about the box, she still believed that it contained some special treat that he was holding back from her.

'I'll show him . . . the old bossy-boots,' she muttered to herself.

Waiting until Epimetheus was out, she managed to talk her way past the guards and into the room. She had stolen the key from beside his bed and nobody thought to stop her. Was she not, after all, the king's wife and the mistress of the house? Her whole body trembling, she knelt down beside the box. It was smaller and older than she had expected. It was also a little surprising (not to say upsetting) that the padlock which fastened it should be in the shape of a human skull. But she was certain it would contain treasure such as would make all her own diamonds and pearls seem like mere pebbles, treasure that would make her the envy of the world. She turned the key and opened the box . . .

. . . and at once all the spites and problems that Epimetheus had for so long kept locked up, exploded into the world. Old age, hard work, sickness . . . they flew out in a great cloud of buzzing, stinging, biting insects. It was as if Pandora had accidentally split the atom. One moment she was standing there with a foolish grin on her face. The next she was screaming in the heart of an intense darkness that had, in seconds, stripped her of her beauty and brought her out in a thousand boils.

At that moment, all the things that make life difficult today, streamed out of Pandora's box and into the world.

Old age, hard work, sickness, vice, anger, envy, lust, covetousness, spite, sarcasm, cynicism, violence, intolerance, injustice, infidelity, famine, drought, pestilence, war, religious persecution, apartheid, taxation, inflation, pollution, unemployment, fascism, racism, sexism, terrorism, communism, nepotism, cubism, patriotism, nihilism, totalitarianism, plagiarism, vandalism, tourism, paranoia, schizophrenia, kleptomania, claustrophobia, xenophobia, hypochondria, insomnia, megalomania, narrow-mindedness, thoughtlessness, selfishness, bribery, corruption, censorship, gluttony, pornography, delinquency, vulgarity, bureaucracy, complacency, obesity, acne, diplomatic immunity, traffic congestion, party political broadcasts, urban development, modern architecture, fast food, muzak, dolphinariums, organized crime, advertising, alcoholism, drug addiction, monosodium glutamate, nicotine, nuclear waste, data processing, fanaticism, insanity, drizzle, elephant's-feet-wastepaper-baskets and much, much more.

At the last moment, Epimetheus managed to slam down the lid, by which time only one thing was left in the box: hope.

Which is just as well. For with all the problems that Pandora had released into the world, where would we be without it?

Pyramus and Thisbe
Retold by Anthony Horowitz

There lived in Babylon, during the reign of Semiramis, two young people whose houses were divided by a single brick wall. Pyramus, who lived on one side of the wall with his parents, was seventeen years old, tall, strong and athletic. Thisbe, who lived on the other side of the wall with her parents, was three years younger, gentle and very beautiful. Not surprisingly, growing up so close to one another, the two of them fell in love. The only trouble was that the two sets of parents could not stand one another.

The reason has never been set on record and in truth it doesn't really matter, for it often happens that neighbours will dislike each other simply because they are neighbours. Perhaps the parents of Thisbe thought their neighbours surly and snobbish. Perhaps the parents of Pyramus thought their neighbours vulgar and churlish. At any rate, they never spoke. If they met in the street they would stride off in opposite directions (even if it meant going out of their way). They never mentioned one another in conversation unless it was to complain. And of course they forbade Pyramus to have anything to do with Thisbe and Thisbe to have anything to do with Pyramus.

Both Pyramus and Thisbe tried to reason with them but, parents being what they are, this proved impossible. In fact they might never have been able to talk to one another had they not discovered a crack in the wall, down at the bottom of the garden. It was not a large crack. If Thisbe squeezed her hand into it, she could just brush the fingertips of Pyramus on the other side. When Pyramus knelt down and looked through it, he could just make out Thisbe's eye gazing back at him on the other side. But at least they could talk through it and every evening they would slip away from the dinner table to swap messages in the cool night air.

But there came a time when Pyramus could bear this separation no longer. Kneeling in the moist grass with his face pressed against the cold stone wall, he sighed so loudly that Thisbe heard him on the other side.

'What is it, my love?' she exclaimed. 'You sound so sad.'

'This is ridiculous,' Pyramus replied. 'Why should we be forced to endure this simply because our parents are so stupid?'

'At least we can talk to each other,' Thisbe said.

'Yes. But it isn't enough. I am seventeen years old – no longer a child. I want to hold you in my arms, close to me. I want to . . .'

'My parents would never allow it!' Thisbe interrupted. 'They call you "that awful boy from next door". I'm not even allowed to mention your name. They have nothing pleasant to say about you.'

'I know all that, but . . .' Even as Pyramus spoke, the idea came to him. 'Why shouldn't we meet? Not here, but outside the city. Surely we can slip away for one night together?'

'Where?' Thisbe asked, her voice trembling.

'The tomb of Ninus. You must know it. There is a temple there, near a stream – just outside the city's boundaries.'

'I know it,' Thisbe whispered. 'But a tomb . . .!'

'This is no time to be superstitious,' Pyramus cried. 'We'll meet there tomorrow night, after supper. There is a mulberry tree near the stream. You can't miss it. We'll meet beneath the tree. Oh Thisbe, my love! For just one night we will be able to hold each other and speak without fear of being overheard.'

'I'll be there!' Thisbe exclaimed. 'Wait for me there, Pyramus. I will come to you.'

And sure enough, the following night, Thisbe wrapped
a shawl around her shoulders and slipped away from her
parents' house, making her way through the city to the
tomb of Ninus. She went with not a little trepidation for
she would have preferred to meet anywhere other than at
a tomb. It was a quiet and secluded spot, well suited to
their secret affair, but somehow it seemed like a bad
omen. She was going to a place of death. Would death be
awaiting her when she got there?

She crossed an ancient copse on the outskirts of the
city, her feet making no sound on the thick carpet of
moss. The moon was full that night, its ivory beams
breaking through the branches and casting a thousand
leafy shadows on the ground below. Now she could hear
the gurgle of a stream and hurrying forward she saw two
marble columns rising smooth and graceful out of the
grass on the edge of a clearing. It was the tomb of Ninus,
and there was the mulberry tree, its fruit as white as snow
in the moonlight. But there was no sign of Pyramus. She
stopped in front of the entrance to the tomb, a great
iron ring hanging just above her head on the wooden
door. Still nobody came. A cloud shaped like a pointed
finger slid in front of the moon. A gust of wind tussled
her hair.

Then she heard the sound, a soft, menacing growl. It
came from the wood. Stepping back, she crouched in the
shadow of the tomb as a great animal padded silently out
from amongst the trees. It was a lioness and it had
recently killed, for the blood was still fresh on its muzzle.

'Oh Pyramus, Pyramus!' Thisbe moaned to herself. She
could hardly move, paralysed with fear.

The lioness heard her. Its head twisted towards her.
Thisbe's hand reached out and tugged at the iron ring set
in the door of the tomb. The door creaked open. Then,
her eyes never leaving the lioness, she stepped backwards

into the blackness of the tomb, slamming the door shut a moment later.

The animal had no intention of harming Thisbe, although she was not to know that. It had eaten already but, hearing the noise, it stalked across the clearing to investigate. Thisbe was out of its sight but as she had reached for the iron ring her shawl had slipped off her shoulders and this the lioness found. As much out of curiosity as anger, it raked at the shawl with its claws, tearing it. A few drops of blood dripped off its mouth, staining it. Then, forgetting all about Thisbe, it re-crossed the clearing and went to the stream to drink.

Meanwhile, Pyramus had been delayed at the supper table by his parents. Although he had asked to be excused several times, they had both had a bad day and were taking it out on him, complaining about his appearance, his lack of ambition, his poor results at school – just about anything they could think of. At last they dismissed him and he was able to steal from the house, make his way through the city and race out to the tomb of Ninus. He didn't stop running until he saw the mulberry tree. At the same moment, he saw the lioness.

The animal, having eaten and drunk, was fast asleep. Lying in the moonlight, you could almost have mistaken it for a statue but for the rise and fall of its stomach and the gleam of blood around its mouth. Pyramus saw the blood. A second later he saw Thisbe's shawl, torn and blood-stained on the grass. He looked back at the lioness. Obviously it had recently feasted. There was no sign of Thisbe. Pyramus raised his head to the sky and wailed.

His parents had denied him love's joy. Now they were unable to spare him love's pain. He felt as if an icc-cold dagger had been plunged into his heart. The life drained out of him – or if not the life then the need to live. It was as if he were suddenly seeing the world in black and white and knew that he would never again understand or experience colour. He had loved Thisbe as much as any man can love any woman and her death made no sense of his life. Worse still, he was to blame. If he had arrived sooner, if he had got there first, then armed with his sword he would have been able to . . .

His sword. He took it from his waist and holding it in both hands, thrust it into his side. He fell back on the grass beneath the mulberry tree. There was no pain but his blood burst out in a fountain, spraying the mulberry fruit. At the same time, a pool of blood formed around him, sinking into the earth and soaking the roots of the tree.

It was then that Thisbe came out of the tomb. She had waited there as long as she could but at last the inky blackness and the damp smell of the grave had driven her out. Slowly she stepped back into the moonlight, searching for the lioness. She frowned. The mulberry tree was still there, but now its fruit was not white but red. What had happened? Pyramus groaned. Thisbe cried out and, forgetting the lioness, ran to him.

Pyramus was dying, but still he was not quite dead. As Thisbe threw herself down beside him, tears streaming down her cheeks, his eyes widened in surprise and he tried to speak. But the words faded on his lips.

'Pyramus!' Thisbe wept. 'What has happened? Tell me! How can this have happened?'

With a trembling hand, Pyramus pointed to the torn shawl. He raised the hand and stroked her cheek. Even now he smiled, feeling her soft flesh without the wall between them. Then his eyes closed and he died.

Thisbe understood what had happened.

'You killed yourself!' she whispered, the tears falling faster. 'You thought me dead and died rather than live without me. But death will not separate us.'

She reached out and grasped the sword, turning it towards her breast. Then she looked up for a last time. Overhead, the stars were sparkling in the night sky.

'I ask the gods only this!' she cried. 'The mulberry tree is stained with my love's blood. May it stay that colour to remind the world of what has happened here.'

She threw herself forward on to the sword.

When their parents discovered the two bodies, they had them cremated and then collected the ashes and mixed them together in a single urn. The gods, too, were moved to pity, for to this day the fruit of the mulberry tree is not white but dark purple, and so it will always be.

Myths: Activities

Reading myths

1 a) What natural phenomenon does the myth *How Winter Came to the Earth* attempt to explain?

b) There are many features that often appear in myths. Find examples of each of the following features in *How Winter Came to the Earth*:

- gods and goddesses
- magic
- imaginary lands
- the battle between good and evil.

2 Read *Izanami and Izanagi*. Explain in your own words how the Japanese myth explains:

a) death

b) population growth.

3 a) Look at *Pandora's Box*. Find and list all the clues that tell us that the box is dangerous.

b) Re-read the description of Pandora's appearance and character (pages 12 and 13) and then explain how they are reflected in her decision to open the box.

4 a) Re-read the story of *Pyramus and Thisbe*. Then copy out and complete the table opposite to show the basic plot and components of the tale.

Hero:	Description	seventeen years old, tall, strong, athletic
Heroine:		
Setting:		
Problem:	their parents' mutual dislike	
Solution:		
Tragedy:		
Result:	mixed together in a single urn	

b) The two sets of parents call each other 'surly and snobbish' and 'vulgar and churlish'. What do you think these words mean? Which ones apply to which parents? What if anything, have the parents learnt by the end of the story?

Original writing

1 Write your own 'myth' explaining a feature of our world. You could explain where rivers come from, why the sky is blue, why the sun rises and sets or you can use your own ideas. You may find it helpful to:

- read the introduction to this section
- plan your myth using a flowchart

empty, dull space above the earth
↓
giant/god/hero
↓
used blue fabric/rainbow/egg shell
↓
sky held up by
↓

2 In *Pandora's Box*, we are not told how Hephaestus came to be crippled, but there are clues in the text that hint at an explanation. Find the clues and use them to come up with a story about how Hephaestus was crippled. Write the story, using about 300 words.

3 Using the components of the Pyramus and Thisbe story that you identified in activity 4 above, write your own story. You can set your story anywhere and at any time. Remember to:

- introduce the hero and heroine, their backgrounds, appearance and character
- explain the problem they are encountering
- devise a solution to the problem
- describe how the plan fails
- explain the tragic outcome and its effect on those left behind.

Section 2
Ghost and Horror

There is a desire in many of us to hear and be frightened by ghost and horror stories. Perhaps it is because they can provide us with ways of thinking about death and the unexplained. They make us confront our fears and uncertainties.

The authors of successful ghost stories use a variety of techniques to create the desired effect on their readers. They often use powerful atmospheres and settings which add to the atmosphere of the action. They also often use the first person ('I') to tell the tales. This may be in order to make the stories more believable, especially if the narrator is initially rational and disbelieving. Sometimes the fact that a character is a ghost is not revealed until later in the story, so that suspense is built up throughout.

Ghost stories can be horrifying, but not all horror stories include ghosts. Horror stories are often about people who have done something they know to be wrong for their own gain. The stories often warn us how lack of judgement or wrongdoing can lead to a terrible fate from which there is no escape. The main feature of a horror story is the creation of fear. The authors use vivid description of settings, events and characters to make the story effective and to evoke terror and dread in their readers.

A Night at a Cottage
Richard Hughes

On the evening that I am considering I passed by some ten or twenty cosy barns and sheds without finding one to my liking: for Worcestershire lanes are **devious** and muddy, and it was nearly dark when I found an empty cottage set back from the road in a little bedraggled garden. There had been heavy rain earlier in the day, and the straggling fruit trees still wept over it.

But the roof looked sound, there seemed no reason why it should not be fairly dry inside – as dry, at any rate, as I was likely to find anywhere.

I decided: and with a long look up the road, and a long look down the road, I drew an iron bar from the lining of my coat and forced the door, which was only held by a padlock and two staples. Inside, the darkness was damp and heavy: I struck a match, and with its haloed light I saw the black mouth of a passage somewhere ahead of me: and then it spluttered out. So I closed the door carefully, though I had little reason to fear passers-by at such a dismal hour in so remote a lane: and lighting another match, I crept down this passage to a little room at the far end, where the air was a bit clearer, for all that the window was boarded across. Moreover, there was a little rusted stove in this room: and thinking it too dark for any to see the smoke, I ripped up part of the **wainscot** with my knife, and soon was boiling my tea over a bright, small fire, and drying some of the day's rain out of my steamy clothes.

---

devious: twisting
wainscot: wooden panelling

Presently I piled the stove with wood to its top bar, and setting my boots where they would best dry, I stretched my body out to sleep.

I cannot have slept very long, for when I woke the fire was still burning brightly. It is not easy to sleep for long together on the level boards of a floor, for the limbs grow numb, and any movement wakes. I turned over, and was about to go again to sleep when I was startled to hear steps in the passage. As I have said, the window was boarded, and there was no other door from the little room – no cupboard even – in which to hide. It occurred to me rather grimly that there was nothing to do but to sit up and face the music, and that would probably mean being **haled** back to Worcester jail, which I had left two bare days before, and where, for various reasons, I had no anxiety to be seen again.

The stranger did not hurry himself, but presently walked slowly down the passage, attracted by the light of the fire: and when he came in he did not seem to notice me where I lay huddled in a corner, but walked straight over to the stove and warmed his hands at it. He was dripping wet; wetter than I should have thought it possible for a man to get, even on such a rainy night; and his clothes were old and worn. The water dripped from him on to the floor: he wore no hat, and the straight hair over his eyes dripped water that sizzled spitefully on the embers.

It occurred to me at once that he was no lawful citizen, but another wanderer like myself; a gentleman of the Road; so I gave him some sort of greeting, and we were presently in conversation. He complained much of the cold and the wet, and huddled himself over the fire, his teeth chattering and his face an ill white.

---

haled: dragged

'No,' I said, 'it is no decent weather for the Road, this. But I wonder this cottage isn't more frequented, for it's a tidy little bit of a cottage.'

Outside the pale dead sunflowers and giant weeds stirred in the rain.

'Time was,' he answered, 'there wasn't a tighter little cot in the county, nor a purtier garden. A regular little parlour, she was. But now no folk'll live in it, and there's very few tramps will stop here either.'

There were none of the rags and tins and broken food about that you find in a place where many beggars are used to stay.

'Why's that?' I asked.

He gave a very troubled sigh before answering.

'Gho-asts,' he said; 'gho-asts. Him that lived here. It is a mighty sad tale, and I'll not tell it you: but the upshot of it was that he drowned himself, down to the mill-pond. All slimy, he was, and floating, when they pulled him out of it. There are fo-aks have seen un floating on the pond, and fo-aks have seen un set round the corner of the school, waiting for his childer. Seems as if he had forgotten, like, how they were all gone dead, and the why he drowned hisself. But there are some say he walks up and down this cottage, up and down; like when the smallpox had 'em, and they couldn't sleep but if they heard his feet going up and down by their doors. Drownded hisself down to the pond, he did; and now he Walks.'

The stranger sighed again, and I could hear the water squelch in his boots as he moved himself.

'But it doesn't do for the like of us to get superstitious,' I answered. 'It wouldn't do for us to get seeing ghosts, or many's the wet night we'd be lying in the roadway.'

'No,' he said; 'no, it wouldn't do at all. I never had belief in Walks myself.'

I laughed.

'Nor I that,' I said. 'I never see ghosts, whoever may.'

He looked at me again in his queer melancholy fashion.

'No,' he said. ''Spect you don't ever. Some folk do-an't. It's hard enough for poor fellows to have no money to their lodging, apart from gho-asts sceering them.'

'It's the coppers, not spooks, make me sleep uneasy,' said I. 'What with coppers, and meddlesome-minded folk, it isn't easy to get a night's rest nowadays.'

The water was still oozing from his clothes all about the floor, and a dank smell went up from him.

'God! man,' I cried, 'can't you NEVER get dry?'

'Dry?' He made a little coughing laughter. 'Dry? I shan't never be dry . . . 'tisn't the likes of us that ever get dry, be it wet OR fine, winter OR summer. See that.'

He thrust his muddy hands up to the wrist in the fire, glowering over it fiercely and madly. But I caught up my two boots and ran crying out into the night.

Who Goes Down This Dark Road?
Joan Aiken

It seems singular, remembering that first interview with Mrs King, to think that I had no kind of premonition or foreknowledge – yet how could I have had? If I had known, or guessed, that my intervention would result in my being brought here – would end in this tedious **incarceration** – I might have let well alone. But I did not.

Amanda King had not made any particular impression on me, save as a very *good* girl. Among the children in the beginners' group she was not distinguished for brightness at her lessons, nor for liveliness in class; she did not have that **spontaneous vivacity** and wit that some small children possess, nor was she in any way remarkable when the children played games, or sang songs, or acted plays, or told stories. And yet, by the time Mrs King came to see me, I was aware of Amanda as a particularly stable and pleasant member of the group. *Stable* seems an odd term to apply to a six-year-old, yet stability seemed to be Amanda's paramount quality. She was always punctual, polite, and friendly; indeed she had charming manners. I had at first assumed that it was Mrs King who prompted the daily – and very tastefully arranged – posies, sometimes from the Kings' garden, sometimes wild flowers; but by degrees I realized that this was Amanda's own idea. Her appearance was in no way striking, yet there was something neat and attractive about her: her dark-blue school pinafore and white blouse were always clean and crisp, her fair hair shining,

---

incarceration: imprisonment
spontaneous vivacity: natural liveliness

beautifully brushed and neatly plaited, her big grey eyes serious and attentive to what was going on. She seemed a model pupil, and, though she never came top in any subject apart from spelling and deportment, seemed unlikely ever to cause either parents or teachers the slightest worry.

It was, therefore, a considerable surprise when Mrs King came to see me, visibly distressed, one afternoon after school when I was setting up the model Saxon village for next day's intermediate class.

'Oh, Mr Thorneycroft, I'm ever so sorry to trouble you when I know how hard you work for the children, but me and Mr King are that worried about Amanda, we don't know what to do for the best.'

'About *Amanda*?' I was really amazed. 'But she's the best little girl in the school.'

'I know, sir, and so she's always been at home, but just lately something's got into her; something – well, peculiar. She's turned that obstinate, sir, I can't give you any idea!'

'Well, even the best children go through awkward phases,' I began vaguely and consolingly. 'What form does it take with Amanda, Mrs King?'

'Sir, it's to do with her hair.'

'Her hair?'

Then it did occur to me that for the last week or two, Amanda's hair had not been so shiningly neat and symmetrically plaited as hitherto. And indeed that very morning, I now recalled, Amanda had turned up with the two corn-blonde plaits shorn off, and her hair hanging loose and rather short about her small serious face. I had made some remark on it and she had said, 'Mum thought it would be easier to keep tidy if it was short.'

The child next to her, Lily Thatcher, called out, 'You oughter sleep with the plaits under your pillow, Mandy, then you'll dream about the fellow you're going to marry!' which raised a laugh, but Amanda, rather oddly, I now recalled, said that she had buried the plaits in the garden.

'What about her hair, then, Mrs King?'

'Well, sir – I don't know how to put it so you won't think either I or the child is crazy – ' I noticed with astonishment that the placid-seeming Mrs King had tears in her eyes – 'but she's got this notion that there's people living in her hair.'

Various possibilities flashed through my mind. I said delicately, 'You're quite sure, Mrs King, that it's not a simple case of nits, head parasites – something like that?'

'Sir! How could you think such a thing? There's some families in the village I wouldn't put it past them, but my Amanda's always been perfectly clean – I've washed her hair myself every Saturday night since she was born.'

'I must say her hair always does look beautifully clean,' I said quickly. 'Well, if that is the case, you don't think it's possible that she *imagines* she has something of the sort? Children sometimes have such odd private worries – '

'No, sir, no, it's not like that. No, it's *people* she says are living on top of her head. In among the hair, like. She says – ' Mrs King faltered, 'she says the hair seems like a forest to them.'

'She's playing a game with you, Mrs King,' I suggested. 'It's just a piece of pretence. I remember when I was a boy I had an imaginary bear – oh, I carried him around with me for years!'

'A game it may be, sir, but it's dead serious to her,' Mrs King said worriedly. 'Every day I have the very deuce of the job, you'll pardon me, sir, to get her hair brushed. "Don't *do* that, Mum, you'll drive them out of the forest," she says, and she screams and screams; it makes my Joe really wild, he's threatened to give her a good hiding if she won't be more reasonable. And lately, sir – oh, I've begun to wonder if she's going mental.' Mrs King here fairly burst out crying. 'She talks such rubbish, sir! All about chariots and temples and sacred stones and armies and navies – it's not right, sir, it really isn't. And sometimes what she says doesn't make sense at all, it's just double-dutch, you can't make head nor tail of it, and she'll go on like that for hours.'

'Did you mention this to Dr Button?'

'Well, I did, sir – I didn't take Amanda to the surgery for fear of scaring her, I just told him, and he fairly snapped my head off and said she was a perfectly healthy child and not to fuss him with a bit of kid's moonshine.'

This sounded true to form. I said cautiously, 'Well, what did you want me to do, Mrs King?'

'Oh, sir, if you could just *talk* to Amanda about it a bit! She thinks the world of you, sir, if you could just reason this nonsense out of her head – '

'Very aptly put, Mrs King.'

She looked at me rather blankly, so I promised that I would see what I could do. 'Supposing I take Amanda for a walk, Mrs King, tomorrow, after school – I could ask her to show me where she picks her delightful bunches of flowers. Then it won't seem too like a formal interview.'

'Oh, Mr Thorneycroft, I don't know how to thank you – '

I pointed out that I hadn't done anything yet, but she went away evidently relieved to have pushed the responsibility on to somebody else, even if only temporarily.

Next afternoon Amanda agreed, with grave politeness, to take me across the Common and show me where she picked her cowslips and ladies' smocks. I thought there was no sense in deferring the question, so as soon as we were away from the village, I said, 'Your mother asked me to talk to you, Amanda, about this idea you have that – er, that people are living in your hair.'

She looked up at me calmly, with a surprisingly adult expression in her grey eyes, and said, 'Yes, I thought perhaps she had.'

I said, gently, not wanting to seem unsympathetic or mocking, 'What sort of people are they, Amanda?'

She answered at once, 'They're a tribe of Gauls, the Veneti. They were defeated, you see, by the Romans, in a big sea-battle, and driven out of their homes. They built a new town, but then it was destroyed – it sank in the sea. And so they collected up what they could of their belongings – and now they live in my hair. It's like a forest to them, you see.'

I was startled, to say the least.

'But, Amanda – how did you come to know about the Veneti?'

'I can hear them,' she said matter-of-factly. 'Talking. Through my skull.'

'But they were a long time ago! More than two thousand years.'

'I suppose they got through it fast, somehow. Some people go quicker than others.'

I said, 'How could they all get on to your head, though? They were full-sized people – a whole tribe of them. How could they all camp on one little corn-coloured nut?'

She gave me a look as closely approaching to impatience as natural politeness would permit.

'Things seem a different size, don't you see, when they're in different places. If I saw you a long way off – you'd look small, wouldn't you? Or if I saw you beside a *huge* monster.' Her eyes widened, and I remembered that, after all, she was still only a six-year-old. The word *relative* was probably outside her vocabulary.

'What sort of language do they talk, these people, Amanda?' This fable she had spun for herself was wonderfully coherent so far; I wondered where she read or heard of the Veneti, who, I recalled, had been vanquished by Caesar in Brittany.

'Well, they talk two languages,' she told me.

'Can you remember any of the words?'

She reeled off a string of jargon which was meaningless to me, full of X sounds and CH sounds; I became more and more interested remembering medical cases of glossolalia, 'speaking with tongues', which sometimes occur in religious fanatics or mental patients – but in an otherwise matter-of-fact little girl of six?

'And what is the other language?'

She then startled me out of my wits by replying, '*Una salus victis nullam sperare salutem*' (There is but one safe thing for the vanquished: not to hope for safety).

'Good heavens, Amanda! Where did you hear that?'

'One of them up there said it.' She pointed to her flaxen locks.

'Can you remember any more?'

'*Quid nunc it per iter tenebricosum – '*

'*Illuc,*' I said it with her, '*unde negant redire quemquam.*'

'You know that too?' she said, turning the grey eyes on me.

'I have heard it, yes. What was the people's town called, Amanda – the town that sank in the sea?'

'It was called Is.'

'Do you know the names of the gods they worship?'

'They must not be spoken or written down. There is a serpent's egg that must be thrown into the air.'

'And caught in a white cloak?'

Quid nunc etc.: that now go down the dark road from which no one is permitted to return

'Yes. But just now their holy men are very worried,' she said, turning to me, frowning – she looked absurdly like her mother.

'Why are they worried, Amanda?'

'They have signs from – from the ones who can tell the future – that there is going to be another very bad happening – and that they are going to have to move again, their circle of sacred stones and all the people with their things. Oh!' she cried, clasping her hands to her fair head, 'I do *hope* Mum isn't going to cut off all my hair! She said she might do that! Please tell her not to, Mr Thorneycroft!'

'All right, Amanda – don't worry. I'll tell her.'

'Look,' she said, cheering up, 'this is where the cowslips grow.'

We both picked a bunch and started for home. I was very silent and thoughtful but Amanda, having had my promise about the hair-cutting, skipped along beside me quite light-heartedly with her bunch of cowslips, humming in a tuneless but not unpleasing little voice.

I, needless to say, was wondering what to do, and hardly looked where I was going. Which is why I didn't hear the car till it was right behind us.

It was young, feckless Colin Gaddock, who works in the petrol station over at Maynards Cross; he always comes home, at a crazy pace, hell-bent on getting to his evening's enjoyment. His wing mirror caught the child's jacket as he shot past us and she was dragged, shrieking, five hundred yards up the road before he could brake to a stop.

He's doing time for manslaughter now; I'd like to think it has taught him a lesson, but fear that he's the kind of hopeless lout who will presently come out of jail and do exactly the same thing again.

I could never go into a butcher's shop again. The sight of a piece of steak . . .

People said I'd had a breakdown, and everyone was very sorry for me. But actually it's simpler than that. What happened was, that the Veneti transferred from Amanda's head to mine.

And I'm a bit bothered now because their Druids are predicting another catastrophe.

Feeding the Dog
Susan Price

This story's supposed to be true.

It's about a witch, one of the really bad kind, a man named Downing.

He'd spent years learning witchcraft, travelling all over the country, to meet other witches and be taught by them. He married a witch's daughter, and they had a horde of children. They kept a pack of cats too, who went out to steal for them, bringing back meat and fish from other people's tables. There were just as many children as there were cats, and some people said that the children *were* the cats; and the only people who doubted this were the people who thought that the children were worse than the cats. Downing and his wife cared just as much for all of them, and anybody who raised hand or stone against either children or cats had to spend the next few days in bed, aching all over, cursed by Witch Downing. And everybody knew that Witch Downing could do worse than make you ache. So, mostly, the little Downings, human and feline, got away with their thieving.

But a farmer named Hollis heard noises in his yard one night, and came out to find three of Downing's children tormenting the pigs in his sty by hitting them with sticks. He shouted at them and told them to go away, and they threw stones at him, and shouted names. Hollis was so angry then that he forgot about Witch Downing. The children were so used to getting away with everything that they didn't try to run away. Hollis laid hold of the eldest and gave him the first hiding he'd ever had in his life. The other two ran away when they saw what was happening to their brother. They ran home and told their father.

Witch Downing went to see Farmer Hollis the next day, and demanded money in compensation for the terrible injuries inflicted on his poor boy. Farmer Hollis was afraid of what he had done, but he wouldn't back down now, and he said, 'What terrible injuries? I've done him no more harm than I've done my own sons – I've only given him the sore backside that he should have had a long time ago from you if you'd been any kind of a father! What favour do you think you're doing him, letting him grow up thinking he can do whatever he pleases?'

'Don't preach at me!' Witch Downing said. He went home, thinking that no curse he'd ever set on anybody before was bad enough for Hollis.

So he made a thing. He killed a couple of his cats, and he caught a big dog, and he killed that too. He used poisons, and some of the worst magic he'd learned, and he made this thing that he called a dog – it looked something like a dog. But it was so black that you couldn't really see it, and its eyes shone all the time like a real dog's eyes do when light catches them – shone red, or green, and sometimes blue. It was big. At midnight Downing said to it, 'Hollis.' The thing went out, and it didn't come back that night. The next day Farmer Hollis was missing from his bed, and couldn't be found anywhere.

Witch Downing boasted that he knew what had happened to Hollis, and that people had better watch out! No one knew what he meant.

That night, Downing woke up and saw two bright green candleflames floating beside his bed. There was a shape around them, a blackness. Then the candle flames burned red, and teeth showed beneath them. It was the thing, the dog, come back. It sat beside Witch Downing's bed and looked at him. When he asked what it wanted, it made no movement or sound, but waited. When Downing tried to leave his bed, it growled, and he lay back quickly. He spoke **incantations** for dismissing spirits, but it stayed. At last he said, 'Farmer Hollis's wife.' Then the thing rose and went out.

People began to disappear. Farmer Hollis had vanished, and then his wife had disappeared the night after. The following day the Vicar couldn't be found; and then a market woman vanished. On the fifth night, the disappearance was of a woman who'd chased the witch's cats away with pepper, and on the sixth night, Farmer Hollis's little son.

But Downing no longer boasted. Now he slunk about and jumped if a dog barked.

People who had nothing much to stay for began to leave the town, and Downing began to run out of names. Night after night the thing came, sat beside his bed, and waited. It was very patient. It waited and waited as Downing, all in a sweat, tried to think of a name he hadn't given it before. Sometimes he kept it waiting almost until morning, and the closer morning came, the more excited the thing was. It panted like a real dog, and stirred where it sat. Downing didn't want to find out what would happen if he kept the thing until morning, and he would gabble out, 'The boy who serves at the greengrocer's!' or 'The girl in the green skirt that I pass in the lane!' And the thing would rise and go out.

Then came a night when Downing, worn out as he was, must have dozed. He woke with a great shock, and saw that the sky was turning pink! And the thing was pacing up and down by his bed, whining with excitement. 'My wife!' Downing cried – and the thing leapt over him and on to his wife. There was a dreadful noise. Downing jumped from the bed and ran away. There was not an eyelash left of his wife when he returned.

---

incantations: spells

But the thing came to his bedside that night; and he could think of no one. When the thing began to wave its tail, he said, 'The baby.' And there was no baby in its cot when Downing got up.

'My eldest son,' he said, the next night; and on nights after that, 'My eldest daughter – Billy – Anne – Mary . . .' And when the last of his children had gone, the thing still came, sat beside him, fixed its eyes on him, and waited.

Downing had nothing to say. Towards dawn, the silence was filled with the drumming of the thing's tail on the floorboards, and a whine from its throat. The light increased – the thing couldn't stay any longer, and its master hadn't fed it. So it ate its master before it left – and who knows where it went, or where it is now?

For all Downing's learning, he had never learned that you can't dine with the Devil without becoming the meal.

The Old Nurse's Story
Elizabeth Gaskell

You know, my dears, that your mother was an orphan, and an only child; and I dare say you have heard that your grandfather was a clergyman up in Westmoreland, where I come from. I was just a girl in the village school, when, one day, your grandmother came in to ask the mistress if there was any scholar there who would do for a nurse-maid; and mighty proud I was, I can tell ye, when the mistress called me up, and spoke to my being a good girl at my needle, and a steady, honest girl, and one whose parents were very respectable, though they might be poor. I thought I should like nothing better than to serve the pretty, young lady, who was blushing as deep as I was, as she spoke of the coming baby, and what I should have to do with it. However, I see you don't care so much for this part of my story, as for what you think is to come, so I'll tell you at once. I was engaged and settled at the parsonage before Miss Rosamond (that was the baby, who is now your mother) was born. To be sure, I had little enough to do with her when she came, for she was never out of her mother's arms, and slept by her all night long; and proud enough was I sometimes when missis trusted her to me. There never was such a baby before or since, though you've all of you been fine enough in your turns; but for sweet, winning ways, you've none of you come up to your mother. She took after her mother, who was a real lady born; a Miss Furnivall, a granddaughter of Lord Furnivall's in Northumberland. I believe she had neither brother nor sister, and had been brought up in my lord's family till she had married your grandfather, who was just a curate, son to a shopkeeper in Carlisle – but a clever, fine gentleman as ever was – and one who was a right-down hard worker in his parish, which was very wide, and scattered all abroad over the Westmoreland Fells. When your mother, little Miss Rosamond, was about four or five years old, both her parents died in a fortnight – one after the other. Ah! that was a sad time. My pretty young mistress and me was looking for another baby, when my master came home from one of his long rides, wet, and tired, and took the fever he died of; and then she never held up her head again, but lived just to see her dead baby, and have it laid on her breast before she sighed away her life. My mistress had asked me, on her death-bed, never to leave Miss Rosamond; but if she had never spoken a word, I would have gone with the little child to the end of the world.

The next thing, and before we had well stilled our sobs, the **executors** and guardians came to settle the affairs. They were my poor young mistress's own cousin, Lord Furnivall, and Mr Esthwaite, my master's brother, a shopkeeper in Manchester; not so well to do then, as he was afterwards, and with a large family rising about him. Well! I don't know if it were their settling, or because of a letter my mistress wrote on her death-bed to her cousin, my lord; but somehow it was settled that Miss Rosamond and me were to go to Furnivall Manor House, in Northumberland, and my lord spoke as if it had been her mother's wish that she should live with his family, and as if he had no objections, for that one or two more or less could make no difference in so grand a household. So, though that was not the way in which I should have wished the coming of my bright and pretty pet to have been looked at – who was like a sunbeam in any family, be it never so grand – I was well pleased that all the folks in

---

executors: people appointed to administer a will

the Dale should stare and admire, when they heard I was going to be young lady's maid at my Lord Furnivall's at Furnivall Manor.

But I made a mistake in thinking we were to go and live where my lord did. It turned out that the family had left Furnivall Manor House fifty years or more. I could not hear that my poor young mistress had ever been there, though she had been brought up in the family; and I was sorry for that, for I should have liked Miss Rosamond's youth to have passed where her mother's had been.

My lord's gentleman, from whom I asked as many questions as I **durst**, said that the Manor House was at the foot of the Cumberland Fells, and a very grand place; that an old Miss Furnivall, a great-aunt of my lord's, lived there, with only a few servants; but that it was a very healthy place, and my lord had thought that it would suit Miss Rosamond very well for a few years, and that her being there might perhaps amuse his old aunt.

I was bidden by my lord to have Miss Rosamond's things ready by a certain day. He was a stern proud man, as they say all the Lords Furnivall were; and he never spoke a word more than was necessary. Folk did say he had loved my young mistress; but that, because she knew that his father would object, she would never listen to him, and married Mr Esthwaite; but I don't know. He never married at any rate. But he never took much notice of Miss Rosamond; which I thought he might have done if he had cared for her dead mother. He sent his gentleman with us to the Manor House, telling him to join him at Newcastle that same evening; so there was no great length of time for him to make us known to all the strangers before he, too, shook us off; and we were left, two lonely young things (I was not eighteen), in the great old Manor House. It seems like yesterday that we drove

---

durst: dared

there. We had left our own dear parsonage very early, and we had both cried as if our hearts would break, though we were travelling in my lord's carriage, which I thought so much of once. And now it was long past noon on a September day, and we stopped to change horses for the last time at a little, smoky town, all full of colliers and miners. Miss Rosamond had fallen asleep, but Mr Henry told me to waken her, that she might see the park and the Manor House as we drove up. I thought it rather a pity; but I did what he bade me, for fear he should complain of me to my lord. We had left all signs of a town, or even a village, and were then inside the gates of a large, wild park – not like the parks here in the south, but with rocks, and the noise of running water, and gnarled thorn-trees, and old oaks, all white and peeled with age.

The road went up about two miles, and then we saw a great and stately house, with many trees close around it, so close that in some places their branches dragged against the walls when the wind blew; and some hung broken down; for no one seemed to take much charge of the place; – to lop the wood, or to keep the moss-covered carriage-way in order. Only in front of the house all was clear. The great oval drive was without a weed; and neither tree nor creeper was allowed to grow over the long, many-windowed front; at both sides of which a wing projected, which were each the ends of other side fronts; for the house, although it was so **desolate**, was even grander than I expected. Behind it rose the Fells, which seemed unenclosed and bare enough; and on the left hand of the house, as you stood facing it, was a little, old-fashioned flower-garden, as I found out afterwards. A door opened out upon it from the west front; it had been scooped out of the thick dark wood for some old Lady Furnivall; but the branches of the great forest trees had

---

desolate: isolated, lonely

grown and overshadowed it again, and there were very few flowers that would live there at that time.

When we drove up to the great front entrance, and went into the hall I thought we should be lost – it was so large, and vast, and grand. There was a chandelier all of bronze, hung down from the middle of the ceiling; and I had never seen one before, and looked at it all in amaze. Then, at one end of the hall, was a great fire-place, as large as the sides of the houses in my country, with massy **andirons and dogs** to hold the wood; and by it were heavy, old-fashioned sofas. At the opposite end of the hall, to the left as you went in – on the western side – was an organ built into the wall, and so large that it filled up the best part of that end. Beyond it, on the same side, was a door; and opposite, on each side of the fire-place, were also doors leading to the east front; but those I never went through as long as I stayed in the house, so I can't tell you what lay beyond.

The afternoon was closing in and the hall, which had no fire lighted in it, looked dark and gloomy, but we did not stay there a moment. The old servant, who had opened the door for us, bowed to Mr Henry, and took us in through the door at the further side of the great organ, and led us through several smaller halls and passages into the west drawing-room, where he said that Miss Furnivall was sitting. Poor little Miss Rosamond held very tight to me, as if she were scared and lost in that great place, and as for myself, I was not much better. The west drawing-room was very cheerful-looking, with a warm fire in it, and plenty of good, comfortable furniture about. Miss Furnivall was an old lady not far from eighty, I should think, but I do not know. She was thin and tall, and had a face as full of fine wrinkles as if they had been drawn all over it with a needle's point. Her eyes were very watchful

---

andirons and dogs: iron supports to hold logs in a fireplace

to make up, I suppose, for her being so deaf as to be obliged to use a trumpet. Sitting with her, working at the same great piece of tapestry, was Mrs Stark, her maid and companion, and almost as old as she was. She had lived with Miss Furnivall ever since they both were young, and now she seemed more like a friend than a servant; she looked so cold, and grey, and stony, as if she had never loved or cared for any one; and I don't suppose she did care for any one, except her mistress; and, owing to the great deafness of the latter, Mrs Stark treated her very much as if she were a child. Mr Henry gave some message from my lord, and then he bowed good-bye to us all – taking no notice of my sweet little Miss Rosamond's outstretched hand – and left us standing there, being looked at by the two old ladies through their spectacles.

I was right glad when they rung for the old footman who had shown us in at first, and told him to take us to our rooms. So we went out of that great drawing-room, and into another sitting-room, and out of that, and then up a great flight of stairs, and along a broad gallery – which was something like a library, having books all down one side, and windows and writing-tables all down the other – till we came to our rooms, which I was not sorry to hear were just over the kitchens; for I began to think I should be lost in that wilderness of a house. There was an old nursery, that had been used for all the little lords and ladies long ago, with a pleasant fire burning in the grate, and the kettle boiling on the hob, and tea things spread out on the table; and out of that room was the night-nursery, with a little crib for Miss Rosamond close to my bed. And old James called up Dorothy, his wife, to bid us welcome; and both he and she were so hospitable and kind, that by and by Miss Rosamond and me felt quite at home; and by the time tea was over, she was sitting on Dorothy's knee, and chattering away as fast as her little tongue could go. I soon found out that Dorothy was from Westmoreland, and that bound her and me together, as it were; and I would never wish to meet with kinder people than were old James and his wife. James had lived pretty nearly all his life in my lord's family, and thought there was no one so grand as they. He even looked down a little on his wife; because, till he had married her, she had never lived in any but a farmer's household. But he was very fond of her, as well he might be. They had one servant under them, to do all the rough work. Agnes they called her; and she and me, and James and Dorothy, with Miss Furnivall and Mrs Stark, made up the family; always remembering my sweet little Miss Rosamond! I used to wonder what they had done before she came, they thought so much of her now. Kitchen and drawing-room, it was all the same. The hard, sad Miss Furnivall, and the cold Mrs Stark, looked pleased when she came fluttering in like a bird, playing and pranking hither and thither, with a continual murmur, and pretty prattle of gladness. I am sure, they were sorry many a time when she flitted away into the kitchen, though they were too proud to ask her to stay with them, and were a little surprised at her taste; though to be sure, as Mrs Stark said, it was not to be wondered at, remembering what stock her father had come of. The great, old rambling house was a famous place for little Miss Rosamond. She made expeditions all over it, with me at her heels; all, except the east wing, which was never opened, and whither we never thought of going. But in the western and northern part was many a pleasant room; full of things that were curiosities to us, though they might not have been to people who had seen more. The windows were darkened by the sweeping boughs of the trees, and the ivy which had over-grown them: but, in the green gloom, we could manage to see old China jars and carved ivory boxes, and great, heavy books, and, above all, the old pictures!

Once, I remember, my darling would have Dorothy go with us to tell us who they all were; for they were all portraits of some of my lord's family, though Dorothy could not tell us the names of every one. We had gone through most of the rooms, when we came to the old state drawing-room over the hall, and there was a picture of Miss Furnivall; or, as she was called in those days, Miss Grace, for she was the younger sister. Such a beauty she must have been! but with such a set, proud look, and such scorn looking out of her handsome eyes, with her eyebrows just a little raised, as if she wondered how any one could have the impertinence to look at her; and her lip curled at us, as we stood there gazing. She had a dress on, the like of which I had never seen before, but it was all the fashion when she was young: a hat of some soft, white stuff like beaver, pulled a little over her brows, and a beautiful plume of feathers sweeping round it on one side; and her gown of blue satin was open in front to a quilted, white stomacher.

'Well, to be sure!' said I, when I had gazed my fill. 'Flesh is grass, they do say; but who would have thought that Miss Furnivall had been such an out-and-out beauty, to see her now?'

'Yes,' said Dorothy. 'Folks change sadly. But if what my master's father used to say was true, Miss Furnivall, the elder sister, was handsomer than Miss Grace. Her picture is here somewhere; but, if I show it you, you must never let on, even to James, that you have seen it. Can the little lady hold her tongue, think you?' asked she.

I was not so sure, for she was such a little, sweet, bold, open-spoken child, so I set her to hide herself; and then I helped Dorothy to turn a great picture, that leaned with its face towards the wall, and was not hung up as the others were. To be sure, it beat Miss Grace for beauty; and, I think, for scornful pride, too, though in that matter it might be hard to choose. I could have looked at it an hour, but Dorothy seemed half frightened at having shown it to me, and hurried it back again, and bade me run and find Miss Rosamond, for that there were some ugly places about the house, where she should like ill for the child to go. I was a brave, high-spirited girl, and thought little of what the old woman said, for I liked hide-and-seek as well as any child in the parish; so off I ran to find my little one.

As winter drew on, and the days grew shorter, I was sometimes almost certain that I heard a noise as if some one was playing on the great organ in the hall. I did not hear it every evening; but, certainly, I did very often; usually when I was sitting with Miss Rosamond, after I had put her to bed, and keeping quite still and silent in the bed-room. Then I used to hear it booming and swelling away in the distance. The first night, when I went down to my supper, I asked Dorothy who had been playing music, and James said very shortly that I was a **gowk** to take the wind **soughing** among the trees for music: but I saw Dorothy look at him very fearfully, and Agnes, the kitchen-maid, said something beneath her breath, and went quite white. I saw they did not like my question, so I held my peace till I was with Dorothy alone, when I knew I could get a good deal out of her. So, the next day, I watched my time, and I coaxed and asked her who it was that played the organ; for I knew that it was the organ and not the wind well enough, for all I had kept silence before James. But Dorothy had had her lesson I'll warrant, and never a word could I get from her. So then I tried Agnes, though I had always held my head rather above her, as I was evened to James and Dorothy, and she was little better than their servant. So she said I must never, never

gowk: fool
soughing: moaning

tell; and if I ever told, I was never to say *she* had told me; but it was a very strange noise, and she had heard it many a time, but most of all on winter nights, and before storms; and folks did say, it was the old lord playing on the great organ in the hall, just as he used to do when he was alive; but who the old lord was, or why he played, and why he played on stormy winter evenings in particular, she either could not or would not tell me. Well! I told you I had a brave heart; and I thought it was rather pleasant to have that grand music rolling about the house, let who would be the player; for now it rose above the great gusts of wind, and wailed and triumphed just like a living creature, and then it fell to a softness most complete; only it was always music, and tunes, so it was nonsense to call it the wind. I thought at first, that it might be Miss Furnivall who played, unknown to Agnes; but, one day when I was in the hall by myself, I opened the organ and peeped all about it and around it, as I had done to the organ in Crosthwaite Church once before, and I saw it was all broken and destroyed inside, though it looked so brave and fine; and then, though it was noon-day, my flesh began to creep a little, and I shut it up, and ran away pretty quickly to my own bright nursery; and I did not like hearing the music for some time after that, any more than James and Dorothy did. All this time Miss Rosamond was making herself more and more beloved. The old ladies liked her to dine with them at their early dinner; James stood behind Miss Furnivall's chair, and I behind Miss Rosamond's all in state; and, after dinner, she would play about in a corner of the great drawing-room, as still as any mouse, while Miss Furnivall slept, and I had my dinner in the kitchen. But she was glad enough to come to me in the nursery afterwards; for, as she said, Miss Furnivall was so sad, and Mrs Stark so dull; but she and I were merry enough; and, by-and-by, I got not to care for that weird rolling music, which did one no harm, if we did not know where it came from.

That winter was very cold. In the middle of October the frosts began, and lasted many, many weeks. I remember, one day at dinner, Miss Furnivall lifted up her sad, heavy eyes, and said to Mrs Stark, 'I am afraid we shall have a terrible winter,' in a strange kind of meaning way. But Mrs Stark pretended not to hear, and talked very loud of something else. My little lady and I did not care for the frost; not we! As long as it was dry we climbed up the steep brows, behind the house, and went up on the Fells, which were bleak, and bare enough, and there we ran races in the fresh, sharp air; and once we came down by a new path that took us past the two old, gnarled holly-trees, which grew about half-way down by the east side of the house. But the days grew shorter, and shorter; and the old lord, if it was he, played away more, and more stormily and sadly on the great organ. One Sunday afternoon – it must have been towards the end of November – I asked Dorothy to take charge of little Missey when she came out of the drawing-room, after Miss Furnivall had had her nap; for it was too cold to take her with me to church, and yet I wanted to go. And Dorothy was glad enough to promise, and was so fond of the child that all seemed well; and Agnes and I set off very briskly, though the sky hung heavy and black over the white earth, as if the night had never fully gone away; and the air, though still, was very biting and keen.

'We shall have a fall of snow,' said Agnes to me. And sure enough even while we were in church, it came down thick, in great, large flakes, so thick it almost darkened the windows. It had stopped snowing before we came out, but it lay soft, thick and deep beneath our feet, as we tramped home. Before we got to the hall the moon rose, and I think it was lighter then – what with the moon, and

what with the white dazzling snow – than it had been
when we went to church, between two and three o'clock.
I have not told you that Miss Furnivall and Mrs Stark never
went to church: they used to read the prayers together, in
their quiet, gloomy way; they seemed to feel the Sunday
very long without their tapestry-work to be busy at. So
when I went to Dorothy in the kitchen, to fetch Miss
Rosamond and take her up-stairs with me, I did not much
wonder when the old woman told me that the ladies had
kept the child with them, and that she had never come to
the kitchen, as I had bidden her, when she was tired of
behaving pretty in the drawing-room. So I took off my
things and went to find her and bring her to her supper
in the nursery. But when I went into the best drawing-
room, there sate the two old ladies, very still and quiet,
dropping out a word now and then, but looking as if
nothing so bright and merry as Miss Rosamond had ever
been near them. Still I thought she might be hiding from
me; it was one of her pretty ways; and that she had
persuaded them to look as if they knew nothing about
her; so I went softly peeping under this sofa, and behind
that chair, making believe I was sadly frightened at not
finding her.

'What's the matter, Hester?' said Mrs Stark sharply. I
don't know if Miss Furnivall had seen me, for, as I told
you, she was very deaf, and she sate quite still, idly staring
into the fire, with her hopeless face. 'I'm only looking for
my little Rosy-Posy,' replied I, still thinking that the child
was there, and near me, though I could not see her.

'Miss Rosamond is not here,' said Mrs Stark. 'She went
away more than an hour ago to find Dorothy.' And she
too turned and went on looking into the fire.

My heart sank at this, and I began to wish I had never
left my darling. I went back to Dorothy and told her.
James was gone out for the day, but she and me and

Agnes took lights and went up into the nursery first, and
then we roamed over the great large house, calling and
entreating Miss Rosamond to come out of her hiding
place, and not frighten us to death in that way. But there
was no answer; no sound.

'Oh!' said I at last. 'Can she have got into the east wing
and hidden there?'

But Dorothy said it was not possible, for that she
herself had never been in there; that the doors were
always locked, and my lord's steward had the keys, she
believed; at any rate, neither she nor James had ever seen
them: so, I said I would go back, and see if, after all, she
was not hidden in the drawing-room, unknown to the old
ladies; and if I found her there, I said, I would whip her
well for the fright she had given me; but I never meant to
do it. Well, I went back to the west drawing-room, and I
told Mrs Stark we could not find her anywhere, and asked
for leave to look all about the furniture there, for I
thought now, that she might have fallen asleep in some
warm, hidden corner; but no! we looked, Miss Furnivall
got up and looked, trembling all over, and she was
nowhere there; then we set off again, every one in the
house, and looked in all the places we had searched
before, but we could not find her. Miss Furnivall shivered
and shook so much, that Mrs Stark took her back into the
warm drawing-room; but not before they had made me
promise to bring her to them when she was found. Well-
a-day! I began to think she never would be found, when I
bethought me to look out into the great front court, all
covered with snow. I was up-stairs when I looked out;
but, it was such clear moonlight, I could see quite plain
two little footprints, which might be traced from the hall
door, and round the corner of the east wing. I don't know
how I got down, but I tugged open the great, stiff hall
door; and, throwing the skirt of my gown over my head

for a cloak, I ran out. I turned the east corner, and there a black shadow fell on the snow; but when I came again into the moonlight, there were the little footmarks going up – up to the Fells. It was bitter cold; so cold that the air almost took the skin off my face as I ran, but I ran on, crying to think how my poor little darling must be **perished** and frightened. I was within sight of the holly-trees, when I saw a shepherd coming down the hill, bearing something in his arms wrapped in his **maud**. He shouted to me, and asked me if I had lost a bairn; and, when I could not speak for crying, he bore towards me, and I saw my wee bairnie lying still, and white, and stiff, in his arms, as if she had been dead. He told me he had been up the Fells to gather in his sheep, before the deep cold of night came on, and that under the holly-trees (black marks on the hill-side, where no other bush was for miles around) he had found my little lady – my lamb – my queen – my darling – stiff, and cold, in the terrible sleep which is frost-begotten. Oh! the joy, and the tears, of having her in my arms once again! for I would not let him carry her; but took her, maud and all, into my own arms, and held her near my own warm neck, and heart, and felt the life stealing slowly back again into her little, gentle limbs. But she was still insensible when we reached the hall, and I had no breath for speech. We went in by the kitchen door.

'Bring the warming-pan,' said I; and I carried her up-stairs and began undressing her by the nursery fire, which Agnes had kept up. I called my little lammie all the sweet and playful names I could think of, – even while my eyes were blinded by my tears; and at last, oh! at length she opened her large, blue eyes. Then I put her into her warm bed, and sent Dorothy down to tell Miss Furnivall

---

perished: frozen
maud: woollen shawl

that all was well; and I made up my mind to sit by my darling's bedside the live-long night. She fell away into a soft sleep as soon as her pretty head had touched the pillow, and I watched by her till morning light; when she wakened up bright and clear – or so I thought at first – and, my dears, so I think now.

She said, that she had fancied that she should like to go to Dorothy, for that both the old ladies were asleep, and it was very dull in the drawing-room; and that, as she was going through the west lobby, she saw the snow through the high window falling – falling – soft and steady; but she wanted to see it lying pretty and white on the ground; so she made her way into the great hall; and then, going to the window, she saw it bright and soft upon the drive; but while she stood there, she saw a little girl, not as old as she was, 'but so pretty,' said my darling, 'and this little girl beckoned to me to come out; and oh, she was so pretty and so sweet, I could not choose but go.' And then this other little girl had taken her by the hand, and side by side the two had gone round the east corner.

'Now you are a naughty little girl, and telling stories,' said I. 'What would your good mamma, that is in heaven, and never told a story in her life, say to her little Rosamond, if she heard her – and I dare say she does – telling stories!'

'Indeed, Hester,' sobbed out my child, 'I'm telling you true. Indeed I am.'

'Don't tell me!' said I, very stern. 'I tracked you by your footmarks through the snow; there were only yours to be seen; and if you had had a little girl to go hand-in-hand with you up the hill, don't you think the footprints would have gone along with yours?'

'I can't help it, dear, dear Hester,' said she, crying, 'if they did not; I never looked at her feet, but she held my hand fast and tight in her little one, and it was very, very cold. She took me up the Fell-path, up to the holly-trees; and there I saw a lady weeping and crying; but when she saw me, she hushed her weeping, and smiled very proud and grand, and took me on her knee, and began to lull me to sleep; and that's all, Hester – but that is true; and my dear mamma knows it is,' said she, crying. So I thought the child was in a fever, and pretended to believe her, as she went over her story – over and over again, and always the same. At last Dorothy knocked at the door with Miss Rosamond's breakfast; and she told me the old ladies were down in the eating parlour, and that they wanted to speak to me. They had both been into the night-nursery the evening before, but it was after Miss Rosamond was asleep; so they had only looked at her – not asked me any questions.

'I shall catch it,' thought I to myself, as I went along the north gallery. 'And yet,' I thought, taking courage, 'it was in their charge I left her; and it's they that's to blame for letting her steal away unknown and unwatched.' So I went in boldly, and told my story. I told it all to Miss Furnivall, shouting it close to her ear; but when I came to the mention of the other little girl out in the snow, coaxing and tempting her out, and willing her up to the grand and beautiful lady by the holly-tree, she threw her arms up – her old and withered arms – cried aloud, 'Oh! Heaven, forgive! Have mercy!'

Mrs Stark took hold of her; roughly enough, I thought; but she was past Mrs Stark's management, and spoke to me, in a kind of wild warning and authority.

'Hester! keep her from that child! it will lure her to her death! That evil child! Tell her it is a wicked, naughty child.' Then, Mrs Stark hurried me out of the room; where, indeed, I was glad enough to go; but Miss Furnivall kept shrieking out, 'Oh! have mercy! Wilt Thou never forgive! It is many a long year ago – '

I was very uneasy in my mind after that. I durst never
leave Miss Rosamond, night or day, for fear lest she might
slip off again, after some fancy or other; and all the more,
because I thought I could make out that Miss Furnivall
was crazy, from their odd ways about her; and I was afraid
lest something of the same kind (which might be in the
family, you know) hung over my darling. And the great
frost never ceased all this time; and, whenever it was a
more stormy night than usual, between the gusts, and
through the wind, we heard the old lord playing on
the great organ. But, old lord, or not, wherever Miss
Rosamond went, there I followed; for my love for her,
pretty, helpless orphan, was stronger than my fear for the
grand and terrible sound. Besides, it rested with me to
keep her cheerful and merry, as beseemed her age. So we
played together, and wandered together, here and there,
and everywhere; for I never dared to lose sight of her
again in that large and rambling house. And so it
happened, that one afternoon, not long before Christmas
day, we were playing together on the billiard-table in the
great hall (not that we knew the right way of playing, but
she liked to roll the smooth ivory balls with her pretty
hands, and I liked to do whatever she did); and, by-and-
by, without our noticing it, it grew dusk indoors, though
it was still light in the open air, and I was thinking of
taking her back into the nursery, when, all of a sudden,
she cried out, –

'Look, Hester! look! there is my poor little girl out in
the snow!'

I turned towards the long, narrow windows, and there,
sure enough, I saw a little girl, less than my Miss
Rosamond – dressed all unfit to be out-of-doors such a
bitter night – crying, and beating against the window-
panes, as if she wanted to be let in. She seemed to sob
and wail, till Miss Rosamond could bear it no longer, and

was flying to the door to open it, when, all of a sudden, and close upon us, the great organ pealed out so loud and thundering, it fairly made me tremble; and all the more, when I remembered me that, even in the stillness of that dead-cold weather, I had heard no sound of little battering hands upon the window-glass, although the Phantom Child had seemed to put forth all its force; and, although I had seen it wail and cry, no faintest touch of sound had fallen upon my ears. Whether I remembered all this at the very moment, I do not know; the great organ sound had so stunned me into terror; but this I know, I caught up Miss Rosamond before she got the hall-door opened, and clutched her, and carried her away, kicking and screaming, into the large, bright kitchen, where Dorothy and Agnes were busy with their mince-pies.

'What is the matter with my sweet one?' cried Dorothy, as I bore in Miss Rosamond, who was sobbing as if her heart would break.

'She won't let me open the door for my little girl to come in; and she'll die if she is out on the Fells all night. Cruel, naughty Hester,' she said, slapping me; but she might have struck harder, for I had seen a look of ghastly terror on Dorothy's face, which made my very blood run cold.

'Shut the back kitchen door fast, and bolt it well,' said she to Agnes. She said no more; she gave me raisins and almonds to quiet Miss Rosamond: but she sobbed about the little girl in the snow, and would not touch any of the good things. I was thankful when she cried herself to sleep in bed. Then I stole down to the kitchen, and told Dorothy I had made up my mind. I would carry my darling back to my father's house in Applethwaite; where, if we lived humbly, we lived at peace. I said I had been frightened enough with the old lord's organ-playing; but now that I had seen for myself this little, moaning child, all decked out as no child in the neighbourhood could be, beating and battering to get in, yet always without any sound or noise – with the dark wound on its right shoulder; and that Miss Rosamond had known it again for the phantom that had nearly lured her to her death (which Dorothy knew was true); I would stand it no longer.

I saw Dorothy change colour once or twice. When I had done, she told me she did not think I could take Miss Rosamond with me, for that she was my lord's ward, and I had no right over her; and she asked me, would I leave the child that I was so fond of, just for sounds and sights that could do me no harm; and that they had all had to get used to in their turns? I was all in a hot, trembling passion; and I said it was very well for her to talk, that knew what these sights and noises betokened, and that had, perhaps, had something to do with the Spectre-Child while it was alive. And I taunted her so, that she told me all she knew, at last; and then I wished I had never been told, for it only made me more afraid than ever.

She said she had heard the tale from old neighbours, that were alive when she was first married; when folks used to come to the hall sometimes, before it had got such a bad name on the country side: it might not be true, or it might, what she had been told.

The old lord was Miss Furnivall's father – Miss Grace, as Dorothy called her, for Miss Maude was the elder, and Miss Furnivall by rights. The old lord was eaten up with pride. Such a proud man was never seen or heard of; and his daughters were like him. No one was good enough to wed them, although they had choice enough; for they were the great beauties of their day, as I had seen by their portraits, where they hung in the state drawing-room. But, as the old saying is, 'Pride will have a fall'; and these two haughty beauties fell in love with the same man, and he no better than a foreign musician, whom their father had down from London to play music with him at the

Manor House. For, above all things, next to his pride, the old lord loved music. He could play on nearly every instrument that ever was heard of: and it was a strange thing it did not soften him; but he was a fierce, dour, old man, and had broken his poor wife's heart with his cruelty, they said. He was mad after music, and would pay any money for it. So he got this foreigner to come; who made such beautiful music, that they said the very birds on the trees stopped their singing to listen. And, by degrees, this foreign gentleman got such a hold over the old lord, that nothing would serve him but that he must come every year; and it was he that had the great organ brought from Holland, and built up in the hall, where it stood now. He taught the old lord to play on it; but many and many a time, when Lord Furnivall was thinking of nothing but his fine organ, and his finer music, the dark foreigner was walking abroad in the woods with one of the young ladies; now Miss Maude, and then Miss Grace.

Miss Maude won the day and carried off the prize, such as it was; and he and she were married, all unknown to any one; and before he made his next yearly visit, she had been confined of a little girl at a farm-house on the Moors, while her father and Miss Grace thought she was away at Doncaster Races. But though she was a wife and a mother, she was not a bit softened, but as haughty and as passionate as ever; and perhaps more so, for she was jealous of Miss Grace, to whom her foreign husband paid a deal of court – by way of blinding her – as he told his wife. But Miss Grace triumphed over Miss Maude, and Miss Maude grew fiercer and fiercer, both with her husband and with her sister; and the former – who could easily shake off what was disagreeable, and hide himself in foreign countries – went away a month before his usual time that summer, and half-threatened that he would never come back again. Meanwhile, the little girl was left

at the farm-house, and her mother used to have her horse
saddled and gallop wildly over the hills to see her once
every week, at the very least – for what she loved, she
loved; and where she hated, she hated. And the old lord
went on playing – playing on his organ; and the servants
thought the sweet music he made had soothed down his
awful temper, of which (Dorothy said) some terrible tales
could be told. He grew infirm too, and had to walk with a
crutch; and his son – that was the present Lord Furnivall's
father – was with the army in America, and the other son
at sea; so Miss Maude had it pretty much her own way,
and she and Miss Grace grew colder and bitterer to each
other every day; till at last they hardly ever spoke, except
when the old lord was by. The foreign musician came
again the next summer, but it was for the last time; for
they led him such a life with their jealousy and their
passions, that he grew weary, and went away, and never
was heard of again. And Miss Maude, who had always
meant to have her marriage acknowledged when her
father should be dead, was left now a deserted wife –
whom nobody knew to have been married – with a child
that she dared not own, although she loved it to
distraction; living with a father whom she feared, and a
sister whom she hated. When the next summer passed
over and the dark foreigner never came, both Miss Maude
and Miss Grace grew gloomy and sad; they had a haggard
look about them, though they looked handsome as ever.
But by-and-by Miss Maude brightened; for her father grew
more and more infirm, and more than ever carried away
by his music; and she and Miss Grace lived almost entirely
apart, having separate rooms, the one on the west side,
Miss Maude on the east – those very rooms which were
now shut up. So she thought she might have her little girl
with her, and no one need ever know except those who
dared not speak about it, and were bound to believe that

it was, as she said, a cottager's child she had taken a fancy to. All this Dorothy said, was pretty well known; but what came afterwards no one knew, except Miss Grace, and Mrs Stark, who was even then her maid, and much more of a friend to her than ever her sister had been. But the servants supposed, from words that were dropped, that Miss Maude had triumphed over Miss Grace, and told her that all the time the dark foreigner had been mocking her with pretended love – he was her own husband; the colour left Miss Grace's cheek and lips that very day for ever, and she was heard to say many a time that sooner or later she would have her revenge; and Mrs Stark was for ever spying about the east rooms.

One fearful night, just after the New Year had come in, when the snow was lying thick and deep, and the flakes were still falling – fast enough to blind any one who might be out and abroad – there was a great and violent noise heard, and the old lord's voice above all, cursing and swearing awfully, – and the cries of a little child, – and the proud defiance of a fierce woman, – and the sound of a blow, – and a dead stillness, – and moans and wailings dying away on the hill-side! Then the old lord summoned all his servants, and told them, with terrible oaths, and words more terrible, that his daughter had disgraced herself, and that he had turned her out of doors – her, and her child, – and that if ever they gave her help, – or food, – or shelter, – he prayed that they might never enter Heaven. And, all the while, Miss Grace stood by him, white and still as any stone; and when he had ended she heaved a great sigh, as much as to say her work was done, and her end was accomplished. But the old lord never touched his organ again, and died within the year; and no wonder! for, on the morrow of that wild and fearful night, the shepherds, coming down the Fell-side, found Miss Maude sitting, all crazy and smiling, under the holly-trees,

nursing a dead child, – with a terrible mark on its
right shoulder. 'But that was not what killed it,' said
Dorothy; 'it was the frost and the cold; – every wild
creature was in its hole, and every beast in its fold, –
while the child and its mother were turned out to wander
on the Fells! And now you know all! and I wonder if
you are less frightened now?'

I was more frightened than ever; but I said I was not. I
wished Miss Rosamond and myself well out of that
dreadful house for ever; but I would not leave her, and I
dared not take her away. But oh! how I watched her, and
guarded her! We bolted the doors, and shut the window-
shutters fast, an hour or more before dark, rather than
leave them open five minutes too late. But my little lady
still heard the weird child crying and mourning; and not
all we could do or say, could keep her from wanting to go
to her, and let her in from the cruel wind and the snow.
All this time, I kept away from Miss Furnivall and Mrs
Stark, as much as ever I could; for I feared them – I knew
no good could be about them, with their grey hard faces,
and their dreamy eyes, looking back into the ghastly years
that were gone. But, even in my fear, I had a kind of pity
– for Miss Furnivall, at least. Those gone down to the pit
can hardly have a more hopeless look than that which
was ever on her face. At last I even got so sorry for her –
who never said a word but what was quite forced from
her – that I prayed for her; and I taught Miss Rosamond to
pray for one who had done a deadly sin; but often when
she came to those words, she would listen, and start up
from her knees, and say, 'I hear my little girl plaining and
crying very sad – Oh! let her in, or she will die!'

One night – just after New Year's Day had come at last,
and the long winter had taken a turn, as I hoped – I heard
the west drawing-room bell ring three times, which was
the signal for me. I would not leave Miss Rosamond

alone, for all she was asleep – for the old lord had been playing wilder than ever – and I feared lest my darling should waken to hear the spectre-child; see her I knew she could not. I had fastened the windows too well for that. So, I took her out of her bed and wrapped her up in such outer clothes as were most handy, and carried her down to the drawing-room, where the old ladies sate at their tapestry-work as usual. They looked up when I came in, and Mrs Stark asked, quite astounded, 'Why did I bring Miss Rosamond there, out of her warm bed?' I had begun to whisper, 'Because I was afraid of her being tempted out while I was away, by the wild child in the snow,' when she stopped me short (with a glance at Miss Furnivall), and said Miss Furnivall wanted me to undo some work she had done wrong, and which neither of them could see to unpick. So, I laid my pretty dear on the sofa, and sate down on a stool by them, and hardened my heart against them, as I heard the wind rising and howling.

Miss Rosamond slept on sound, for all the wind blew so; and Miss Furnivall said never a word, nor looked round when the gusts shook the windows. All at once she started up to her full height, and put up one hand, as if to bid us listen.

'I hear voices!' she said. 'I hear terrible screams – I hear my father's voice!'

Just at that moment, my darling wakened with a sudden start: 'My little girl is crying, oh, how she is crying!' and she tried to get up and go to her, but she got her feet entangled in the blanket, and I caught her up; for my flesh had begun to creep at these noises, which they heard while we could catch no sound. In a minute or two the noises came, and gathered fast, and filled our ears; we, too, heard voices and screams, and no longer heard the winter's wind that raged abroad. Mrs Stark looked at me, and I at her, but we dared not speak. Suddenly Miss

Furnivall went towards the door, out into the ante-room, through the west lobby, and opened the door into the great hall. Mrs Stark followed, and I durst not be left, though my heart almost stopped beating for fear. I wrapped my darling tight in my arms, and went out with them. In the hall the screams were louder than ever; they sounded to come from the east wing – nearer and nearer – close on the other side of the locked-up doors – close behind them. Then I noticed that the great bronze chandelier seemed all alight, though the hall was dim, and that a fire was blazing in the vast hearth-place, though it gave no heat; and I shuddered up with terror, and folded my darling closer to me. But as I did so, the east door shook, and she, suddenly struggling to get free from me, cried, 'Hester! I must go! My little girl is there; I hear her; she is coming! Hester, I must go!'

I held her tight with all my strength; with a set will, I held her. If I had died, my hands would have grasped her still, I was so resolved in my mind. Miss Furnivall stood listening, and paid no regard to my darling, who had got down to the ground, and whom I, upon my knees now, was holding with both my arms clasped round her neck; she still striving and crying to get free.

All at once, the east door gave way with a thundering crash, as if torn open in a violent passion, and there came into that broad and mysterious light, the figure of a tall, old man, with grey hair and gleaming eyes. He drove before him, with many a relentless gesture of **abhorrence**, a stern and beautiful woman, with a little child clinging to her dress.

'Oh Hester! Hester!' cried Miss Rosamond. 'It's the lady! the lady below the holly-trees; and my little girl is with her. Hester! Hester! let me go to her; they are drawing me to them. I feel them – I feel them. I must go!'

---

abhorrence: disgust

Again she was almost convulsed by her efforts to get away; but I held her tighter and tighter, till I feared I should do her a hurt; but rather that than let her go towards those terrible phantoms. They passed along towards the great hall-door, where the winds howled and ravened for their prey; but before they reached that, the lady turned; and I could see that she defied the old man with a fierce and proud defiance; but then she quailed – and then she threw her arms wildly and piteously to save her child – her little child – from a blow from his uplifted crutch.

And Miss Rosamond was torn as by a power stronger than mine, and writhed in my arms, and sobbed (for by this time the poor darling was growing faint).

'They want me to go with them on to the Fells – they are drawing me to them. Oh, my little girl! I would come, but cruel, wicked Hester holds me very tight.' But when she saw the uplifted crutch she swooned away, and I thanked God for it. Just at this moment – when the tall, old man, his hair streaming as in the blast of a furnace, was going to strike the little, shrinking child – Miss Furnivall, the old woman by my side, cried out, 'Oh, father! father! spare the little, innocent child!' But just then I saw – we all saw – another phantom shape itself, and grow clear out of the blue and misty light that filled the hall; we had not seen her till now, for it was another lady who stood by the old man, with a look of relentless hate and triumphant scorn. That figure was very beautiful to look upon, with a soft, white hat drawn down over the proud brows, and a red and curling lip. It was dressed in an open robe of blue satin. I had seen that figure before. It was the likeness of Miss Furnivall in her youth; and the terrible phantoms moved on, regardless of old Miss Furnivall's wild entreaty, – and the uplifted crutch fell on the right shoulder of the little child, and the younger sister looked on, stony and deadly serene. But at that moment, the dim lights, and the fire that gave no heat, went out of themselves, and Miss Furnivall lay at our feet stricken down by the **palsy** – death-stricken.

Yes! she was carried to her bed that night never to rise again. She lay with her face to the wall, muttering low, but muttering alway: 'Alas! alas! what is done in youth can never be undone in age! What is done in youth can never be undone in age!'

---

palsy: paralysis

Ghost and Horror: Activities

Reading ghost and horror stories

1 a) Re-read *A Night at a Cottage*. List the words and phrases that describe:
- the cottage
- the location of the cottage
- the atmosphere inside the cottage
- the appearance of the stranger
- the narrator's attitude towards the stranger.

b) How does the narrator feel at each of the following points of the story? Use your notes from 1a) to help you.
- the finding of the cottage
- the finding of the dry room
- hearing footsteps in the passage
- seeing the stranger
- seeing the stranger put his hands into the fire.

2 a) Now look at *Who Goes Down This Dark Road?* Like *A Night at a Cottage*, this story is written in the first person ('I'). Discuss why you think the authors chose to write in the first person. In what ways are the narrators of the two stories similar and in what ways are they different? Think about:
- who they are and what they do
- why they are telling the story
- whether they believe in ghosts at the beginning of the story

- whether they believe in ghosts at the end of the story
- the language each uses to tell his story.

b) In *Who Goes Down This Dark Road?*, there are no particularly 'ghostly' incidents, but Joan Aiken still manages to make the story disturbing. This may be because of the following details:
- the fact that the victim, Amanda, is a child
- the adults' refusal to believe Amanda's story
- the vague way the accident is described
- who the ghosts might be
- what the last sentence suggests.

Choose **two** of the above features which you find most horrific or disturbing. Present a short talk to your group explaining how the points you have chosen put this story in the Ghost and Horror genre.

3 a) *Feeding the Dog* begins, 'This story is supposed to be true'. Why do you think Susan Price uses the word 'supposed' here? Does the narrator want the reader to believe the story? Explain your answer.

b) What other reasons might there be for telling the story? Discuss possible reasons for ending the story with 'For all Downing's learning, he had never learned that you can't dine with the Devil without becoming the meal'. What do you think is meant by this?

4 In *The Old Nurse's Story*, the ghost of the little girl is not mentioned until page 59. But we do feel as though there is something strange and frightening about the story well before then.

Give examples of the way Elizabeth Gaskell builds up the ghostly atmosphere before the first appearance of the ghost. You may like to think about:

- the fact that it is a 'true' account written in the first person
- the nurse's fear of other people in the story
- the description of the house and rooms
- the use of the seasons and the weather
- the characters and descriptions of Miss Furnivall and Mrs Stark
- the strange music
- the mystery surrounding the picture of the elder sister.

Original writing

1 Many 'haunted houses' are open to tourists. Imagine that you own a haunted house and want to publicize it in the local newspaper. Design an advert to attract tourists. Include details of:

- the name and location of the house
- who – or what – it is haunted by
- why it is haunted
- what visitors are likely to see and/or hear
- cost and times of entry
- any other details that you think would be persuasive.

2 Read the last two paragraphs of *Who Goes Down This Dark Road?* Then write a short story in which the narrator tries to convince his family and friends of what has happened to him. You will need to think about the kind of catastrophe the Druids are predicting, whether it actually happens and whether you think the narrator manages to survive it.

3 a) Look at the passage on page 39 which describes how Witch Downing made the dog. List those words and phrases in the story which make the animal appear like a dog. Then list those words and phrases in the story that show it is not a dog.

   b) Now invent your own creature of revenge. Write a couple of paragraphs describing your creature. Explain how it was made, what it looks like and what it does.

4 In *The Old Nurse's Story*, Miss Furnivall feels very guilty about how she treated her sister and her sister's child – 'What is done in youth can never be undone in age.' Write a short passage saying whether you agree with this or not. Think about things you did when you were younger that you are since ashamed of, how you tried to put them right and whether or not you succeeded.

Section 3
Science Fiction

Science fiction is not a new genre. People have been interested for a very long time in what the future might hold for them – H. G. Wells was writing science fiction one hundred years ago.

Through this type of writing, writers are able to speculate about future scientific progress and its possibilities and dangers. The stories often look at new ideas and concerns and investigate how they might develop. They can examine how these developments might get out of control and what the effects could be.

There are some elements which occur in many science fiction stories. As the stories often refer to events, objects and technology which do not exist at the time of writing, the writers need to invent new terms and names for them. Frequently stories are written in the third person ('he'/ 'she') and include a lot of technological description.

Many science fiction stories are concerned with aliens, space travel and worlds beyond Earth. Others portray a picture of our society here in the future. In all kinds of successful science fiction, the writers use their imagination to look forward, but also to reflect the concerns and values of the present.

A Gnaw of Rats
Robert Swindells

An ordinary house, it was. Just an ordinary, empty house with all its windows broken. Once it had stood on the edge of town but the town had grown bigger, and now blocks of flats looked down into its tangled garden. Nobody had lived there for a long time. Nobody, that is, except the rats.

The rats moved in one wet, windy night, one hundred of them, led by Old Smog. They went straight to the cellars, where Old Smog stood on an upturned, rusty pail and said, 'You are the First Gnaw. A gnaw is a hundred rats. If you were sheep, you would be called a flock. If you were people . . .'.

At the word 'people', the rats shuffled restlessly, and one or two of them squealed with anger.

'. . . If you were people you would be called a crowd, or perhaps a regiment. But you are rats. A gnaw of rats.' He paused, looking all around. 'This house,' he continued, 'is now the base of the First Gnaw, and Supreme Headquarters of the World-wide Rat Army.'

A young rat got up on its hind legs and rested its hands on the pail, gazing up at Old Smog. 'Please,' it said. 'What is the World-wide Rat Army? I've never heard of it.'

'Neither have I,' said a voice in the crowd.

'Me neither,' said another rat. A muttering broke out.

'Silence!' cried Festus. He was Old Smog's assistant. 'Listen to your leader.'

Old Smog waited until they were all silent.

'The World-wide Rat Army begins tonight,' he said. 'It begins here.' His eyes swept the grey throng of rats. 'Where are my Scouters?'

Several young rats began pushing their way to the front.

'Ah!' growled Old Smog. 'There you are. Now listen. I have a task for you.'

The Scouter-rats listened.

'I want you to go out among the people,' he began.

'Aaah!' went all the hundred rats. Festus frowned at them.

'I want you to find me ten people who travel the world,' said Old Smog. 'They must be people who, between them, visit every country on earth. When you have found them, and know where each of them lives, report to me here. Go now.'

The Scouter-rats left, and Old Smog turned back to the ninety who remained. 'For a thousand years,' he cried, 'the people have trapped us, poisoned us, shot at us and turned their dogs on us.'

'Yes!' cried all the rats.

'They have told wicked stories about us, and used us in cruel experiments.'

'Yes!' shouted the rats again.

'Now it is our turn!'

'Hoorah!' they yelled.

'We will have our victory,' he cried. 'But it will not happen overnight. It will take patience and planning, and plenty of hard work by everyone.'

'We're ready!' cried a voice.

'Yes!' chorused the Gnaw. 'We're ready!'

'Very well.' Old Smog looked down on them, his eyes moving from one eager face to another. 'Here is the plan. We shall carry a plague to the people.'

'Aaah!' went all the rats.

'It has been done before,' said Old Smog. 'Long ago, by our cousins the black rats. They carried a plague to the people. There was no cure. The people could do nothing. Millions died. He gazed down at his audience. 'They called it the Black Death,' he cried. 'It spread from person to person, from town to town and from country to country; but . . .' He stopped. The rats gazed up at him. 'Travel was slow in those days. There were no motor cars, no locomotives, no aeroplanes. The plague spread a long way, but it travelled slowly and in the end it died out.'

A long sigh rippled through the Gnaw.

'This time, things will be different. Think of it.' Old Smog's whiskers quivered. 'A man gets on board a jumbo jet. He has the plague, but he doesn't know it yet. During the flight, he sneezes. That sneeze has fifty million plague germs in it. The jumbo jet carries two hundred people. They breathe in the germs.

'The plane lands at Frankfurt. A few passengers get off, and a few new ones get on. Our friend is still sneezing. He thinks he's getting a cold. The plane flies on to Rome. Again, some of the passengers leave the plane and new ones join it. It takes off for Athens. Another exchange of passengers. And after Athens: Beirut, Karachi, Singapore and Sydney.

'In Sydney, our friend becomes critically ill and dies. But by then he has carried the plague across half the world.'

As Old Smog stopped speaking, the assembled rats began to leap around, hugging one another and screaming with joy.

'Silence!' shrieked Festus. He had joined his leader on the pail. The commotion gradually subsided.

'That is not all,' continued Old Smog. 'My Scouters will find *ten* such persons. Within two weeks, the plague will have spread throughout the world. It will not be stopped by oceans, as the old plague was. But . . .' Again he paused, looking down at his followers.

'We must remember that now there is a cure for the plague. For that reason, it will not be enough for us to begin its spread. We must also make sure that the people cannot protect themselves with injections. We must see to it that their hospitals stop working. We must deny them food, transport, electricity and clean water. We must attack them on every front!'

This time the roar was deafening. It drowned Festus's voice, and it was some time before order was restored.

'I shall need volunteers,' went on Old Smog, as soon as he could make himself heard. 'I shall ask for Breeder-rats first of all. These rats will swell our numbers for the great work ahead. Then I shall require Carrier-rats, to carry the plague to the ten people my Scouters pick out. Next, I want Demolition-rats and Spoiler-rats. The Demolition-rats will strike at water-mains, electricity cables, drains, buildings and vehicle tyres. The Spoiler-rats will go out into the countryside and attack the crops, eating what they can and spoiling the rest. They will also attack warehouses where food is stored. Finally, I shall need more Scouter-rats, to lead gnaws in countries throughout the world and report back to me.'

The rats were wild with excitement, and there was no shortage of volunteers. Within half an hour, all of them had been set a task, and the meeting ended.

Two weeks later, the Scouters had tracked down the travellers and the Carrier-rats slipped away to do their dreadful work.

Ten days passed. In the derelict house, the rats waited. Then a man died in hospital in Singapore. He had flown in from England, and he had the plague. The next day a woman was taken from a plane at New York, critically ill. She died within hours. Desperate attempts were made to trace and isolate every passenger who had flown with these two victims, but it was impossible. They had dispersed, carrying with them the fatal infection.

The plague spread like wildfire. Soon hospitals everywhere were filled with its victims. Doctors and nurses, reeling with exhaustion, worked round the clock.

Then the Demolition-rats struck. Pouring in their thousands from drains and sewers, they gnawed their way into the wall-cavities of hospitals, clinics and laboratories. They chewed at the plastic sheathing of electricity cables, bit through the wires and blacked out the buildings. They shredded the tyres of ambulances so that patients could not be evacuated from cold, dark wards. The cities became reeking beds of infection as the rats dammed up sewer-pipes and broke water-mains beneath the streets.

Citizens fled for the open countryside, only to find themselves under attack from starving country people whose crops had been decimated by the rats.

World-wide panic ensued. In a desperate fight for clean water, food and shelter, the people turned on one another, and many of those who escaped the plague died at the hands of their neighbours.

Old Smog sat in the cellar of the derelict house. All around it were empty tenements whose doors and windows creaked and banged in the wind. Sometimes a ragged figure would appear in the street, searching frantically for something, anything to eat. Then the rats would scrabble up cellar-grate and sewer-pipe. A thousand hate-filled eyes would follow the scavenger's progress until, at a word from their leader, they would surge forth in a screaming horde to pull him down.

After a while, there were no more ragged figures. A great silence descended on Earth. The rats came out of hiding. For the first time in a thousand years they moved in sunlight, unafraid. The people were gone. Their dogs were gone too, and their cats.

Old Smog came up out of his cellar and stood on top of a rotting car. He looked all around and saw rats; rats in every direction as far as he could see. They began to cheer. Old Smog waved to them, beaming. Even Festus smiled.

The cheering went on for a long time. At last the rats could cheer no more, and Old Smog began to speak.

'All of this,' he said, making a great sweep with his paw, 'is yours. The whole world is yours. You have fought for it, and you have won. It is yours. Go now, and do with it what you will. But . . .' He drew himself up to his full height, and they waited. 'Remember who led you. Remember whose plan it was. Remember Old Smog!'

'Old Smog!' they howled. 'Old Smog, Old Smog, Old Smog.'

A year went by. The rats lived in the houses. It was better than living in sewers. When they were hungry, they fed at rubbish tips or went out into the country to eat apples and corn and chickens.

Another year passed, and then another. Some of the houses had broken windows now, or slates missing from their roofs. Rain got in. Little toadstools started growing on the carpets. It was nearly as cold inside as it was on the street. There wasn't much left on the rubbish tips either, and when they went out into the country, the rats found that corn didn't grow much any more. The chickens seemed to have gone, and most of the apples had worms in them.

They began to feel cold, and a little hungry.

Another year went by. The houses were beginning to fall down and there was almost no food. The rats muttered against Old Smog, but there was nothing he could do. Rats are good at destroying things, but they cannot make anything, except more rats. There were more and more rats now, and less and less food. Some of the rats were dying.

One day, some thin, angry rats rushed into Old Smog's house, bit him to death and ate him. They ate Festus, too. Now they had no leader. They did not know what to do.

All over the world, afraid and thin, the rats were saying, 'Who will show us what to do? Who will be our leader?'

Then, on a misty morning near a town called Hamelin, a hole appeared in a hillside. A man stepped out of the hole, and looked all around. He smiled at the stillness. If there had been anyone to see him, they might have laughed at the clothes he wore; but there was no one. They were gone at last, the greedy ones. The lovers of gold. All gone. It was time. The children of the hill could wake now, and come out into the world. *They* would not value gold more than life. Not the children of the hill. But first . . .

He drew a wooden pipe from his belt, raised it to his lips, and set off down the hill.

In the ruins of the town below, the rats paused in their scavenging. A shiver ran through every rat, and from rat to rat the message rang: 'A leader. We have a leader. He is come.' They seemed not to notice that the new leader looked very like their former enemy.

Swarming out of sewers, cellars and dustbins, they followed the stream of music that beckoned them towards the wide, deep river.

The Star Ducks
Bill Brown

Ward Rafferty's long sensitive newshawk's nose alerted him for a hoax as soon as he saw the old Alsop place. There was no crowd of curious farmers standing around, no ambulance.

Rafferty left *The Times* press car under a walnut tree in the drive and stood for a moment noting every detail with the efficiency that made him *The Times*' top reporter. The old Alsop house was brown, weathered, two-storey with cream-coloured **filigree** around the windows and a lawn that had grown up to weeds. Out in back were the barn and chicken houses and fences that were propped up with boards and pieces of pipe. The front gate was hanging by one hinge but it could be opened by lifting it. Rafferty went in and climbed the steps, careful for loose boards.

Mr Alsop came out on the porch to meet him. 'Howdy do,' he said.

Rafferty pushed his hat back on his head the way he always did before he said: 'I'm Rafferty of *The Times*.' Most people knew his by-line and he liked to watch their faces when he said it.

'Rafferty?' Mr Alsop said, and Rafferty knew he wasn't a *Times* reader.

'I'm a reporter,' Rafferty said. 'Somebody phoned in and said an airplane cracked up around here.'

Mr Alsop looked thoughtful and shook his head slowly.

'No,' he said.

---

filigree: ornamental metalwork

Rafferty saw right away that Alsop was a slow thinker so he gave him time, mentally **pegging** him a **taciturn** Yankee. Mr Alsop answered again, 'Noooooooooooo.'

The screen door squeaked and Mrs Alsop came out. Since Mr Alsop was still thinking, Rafferty repeated the information for Mrs Alsop, thinking she looked a little brighter than her husband. But Mrs Alsop shook her head and said, 'Noooooooooooo,' in exactly the same tone Mr Alsop had used.

Rafferty turned around with his hand on the porch railing ready to go down the steps.

'I guess it was just a phony tip,' he said. 'We get lots of them. Somebody said an airplane came down in your field this morning, straight down trailing fire.'

Mrs Alsop's face lighted up. 'Ohhhhhhhhhh!' she said. 'Yes it did, but it wasn't wrecked. Besides, it isn't really an airplane. That is, it doesn't have wings on it.'

Rafferty stopped with his foot in the air over the top step. 'I beg your pardon?' he said. 'An airplane came down? And it didn't have wings?'

'Yes,' Mrs Alsop said. 'It's out there in the barn now. It belongs to some folk who bend iron with a hammer.'

This, Rafferty thought, begins to smell like news again.

'Oh, a helicopter,' he said.

Mrs Alsop shook her head. 'No, I don't think it is. It doesn't have any of those fans. But you can go out to the barn and have a look. Take him out, Alfred. Tell him to keep on the walk because it's muddy.'

'Come along,' Mr Alsop said brightly. 'I'd like to look the contraption over again myself.'

Rafferty followed Mr Alsop around the house on the board walk thinking he'd been mixed up with some queer people in his work, some crackpots and some screwballs,

---

pegging: marking down
taciturn: reluctant to speak

some imbeciles and some lunatics, but for sheer dumbness, these Alsops had them all beat.

'Got a lot of chickens this year,' Mr Alsop said. 'All fine stock. Minorcas. Sent away for roosters and I've built a fine flock. But do you think chickens'll do very well up on a star, Mr Rafferty?'

Rafferty involuntarily looked up at the sky and stepped off the boards into the mud.

'Up on a what?'

'I said up on a star.' Mr Alsop had reached the barn door and was trying to shove it open. 'Sticks,' he said. Rafferty put his shoulder to it and the door slid. When it was open a foot, Rafferty looked inside and he knew he had a story.

The object inside looked like a giant plastic balloon only half inflated so that it was globular on top and its flat bottom rested on the straw-covered floor. It was just small enough to go through the barn door. Obviously it was somebody's crackpot idea of a space ship, Rafferty thought. The headline that flashed across his mind in **thirty-six point Bodoni** was 'Local Farmer Builds Rocket Ship For Moon Voyage'.

'Mr Alsop,' Rafferty said hopefully, 'you didn't build this thing, did you?'

Mr Alsop laughed. 'Oh, no, I didn't build it. I wouldn't know how to build one of those things. Some friends of ours came in it. Gosh, I wouldn't even know how to fly one.'

Rafferty looked at Mr Alsop narrowly and he saw the man's face was serious.

'Just who are these friends of yours, Mr Alsop?' Rafferty asked cautiously.

'Well, it sounds funny,' Mr Alsop said, 'but I don't rightly know. They don't talk so very good. They don't talk at all.

---

thirty-six point Bodoni: large newspaper typeface

All we can get out of them is that their name is something about bending iron with a hammer.

Rafferty had been circling the contraption, gradually drawing closer to it. He suddenly collided with something he couldn't see. He said, 'ouch' and rubbed his shin.

'Oh, I forgot to tell you, Mr Rafferty,' Mr Alsop said, 'they got a gadget on it that won't let you get near, some kind of a wall you can't see. That's to keep boys away from it.'

'These friends of yours, Mr Alsop, where are they now?'

'Oh, they're over at the house,' Mr Alsop said. 'You can see them if you want to. But I think you'll find it pretty hard talking to them.'

'Russians?' Rafferty asked.

'Oh, no, I don't think so. They don't wear cossacks.'

'Let's go,' Rafferty said in a low voice and led the way across the muddy barnyard toward the house.

'The folks come here the first time about six years ago,' Mr Alsop said. 'Wanted some eggs. Thought maybe they could raise chickens up where they are. Took 'em three years to get home. Eggs spoiled. So the folks turned right around and came back. This time I fixed 'em up a little **brooder** so they can raise chickens on the way home.' He suddenly laughed. 'I can just see that little contraption way out there in the sky full of chickens.'

Rafferty climbed up on the back porch ahead of Mr Alsop and went through the back door into the kitchen. Mr Alsop stopped him before they went into the living room.

'Now, Mr Rafferty, my wife can talk to these people better than I can, so anything you want to know you better ask her. Her and the lady get along pretty good.'

'Okay,' Rafferty said. He pushed Mr Alsop gently through the door into the living room, thinking he would play along, act naïve.

---

brooder: incubator

Mrs Alsop sat in an armchair close to a circulating heater. Rafferty saw the visitors sitting side by side on the davenport, he saw them waving their long, flexible antennae delicately, he saw their lavender faces as expressionless as glass, the round eyes that seemed to be painted on.

Rafferty clutched the door facing and stared.

Mrs Alsop turned toward him brightly.

'Mr Rafferty,' she said, 'these are the people that came to see us in that airplane.' Mrs Alsop raised her finger and both the strangers bent their antennae down in her direction.

'This is Mr Rafferty,' Mrs Alsop said. 'He's a newspaper reporter. He wanted to see your airplane.'

Rafferty managed to nod and the strangers curled up their antennae and nodded politely. The woman scratched her side with her left claw.

Something inside Rafferty's head was saying, you're a smart boy, Rafferty, you're too smart to be taken in. Somebody's pulling a whopping, skilful publicity scheme, somebody's got you down for a sucker. Either that or you're crazy or drunk or dreaming.

Rafferty tried to keep his voice casual.

'What did you say their names are, Mrs Alsop?'

'Well, we don't know,' Mrs Alsop said. 'You see they can only make pictures for you. They point those funny squiggly horns at you and they just think. That makes you think, too – the same thing they're thinking. I asked them what their name is and then I let them think for me. All I saw was a picture of the man hammering some iron on an anvil. So I guess their name is something like Man-Who-Bends-Iron. Maybe it's kind of like an Indian name.'

Rafferty looked slyly at the people who bent iron and at Mrs Alsop.

'Do you suppose,' he said innocently, 'they would talk to me – or *think* to me?'

Mrs Alsop looked troubled.

'They'd be glad to, Mr Rafferty. The only thing is, it's pretty hard at first. Hard for you, that is.'

'I'll try it,' Rafferty said. He took out a cigarette and lighted it. He held the match until it burned his fingers.

'Just throw it in the coal bucket,' Mr Alsop said.

Rafferty threw the match in the coal bucket.

'Ask these things . . . a . . . people where they come from,' he said.

Mrs Alsop smiled. 'That's a very hard question. I asked them that before but I didn't get much of a picture. But I'll ask them again.'

Mrs Alsop raised her finger and both horns bent toward her and aimed directly at her head.

'This young man,' Mrs Alsop said in a loud voice like she was talking to someone hard of hearing, 'wants to know where you people come from.'

Mr Alsop nudged Rafferty. 'Just hold up your finger when you want your answer.'

Rafferty felt like a complete idiot but he held up his finger. The woman whose husband bends iron bent her antenna down until it focused on Rafferty between the eyes. He involuntarily braced himself against the door facings. Suddenly his brain felt as though it were made of rubber and somebody was wringing and twisting and pounding it all out of shape and moulding it back together again into something new. The terror of it blinded him. He was flying through space, through a great white void. Stars and meteors whizzed by and a great star, dazzling with brilliance, white and sparkling, stood there in his mind and then went out. Rafferty's mind was released but he found himself trembling, clutching the door facings. His burning cigarette was on the floor. Mr Alsop stooped and picked it up.

'Here's your cigarette, Mr Rafferty. Did you get your answer?'

Rafferty was white.

'Mr Alsop!' he said. 'Mrs Alsop! This is on the level. These creatures are really from out there in space somewhere!'

Mr Alsop said: 'Sure, they come a long way.'

'Do you know what this means?' Rafferty heard his voice becoming hysterical and he tried to keep it calm. 'Do you know this is the most important thing that has ever happened in the history of the world? Do you know this is . . . yes it is, it's the biggest story in the world and it's happening to me, do you understand?' Rafferty was yelling. 'Where's your phone?'

'We don't have a telephone,' Mr Alsop said. 'There's one down at the filling station. But these people are going to go in a few minutes. Why don't you wait and see them off? Already got their eggs and the brooder and feed on board.'

'No!' Rafferty gasped. 'They can't go in a few minutes! Listen, I've got to phone – I've got to get a photographer!'

Mrs Alsop smiled.

'Well, Mr Rafferty, we tried to get them to stay over for supper but they have to go at a certain time. They have to catch the tide or something like that.'

'It's the moon,' Mr Alsop said with authority. 'It's something about the moon being in the right place.'

The people from space sat there demurely, their claws folded in their laps, their antennae neatly curled to show they weren't eavesdropping on other people's minds.

Rafferty looked frantically around the room for a telephone he knew wasn't there. Got to get Joe Pegley at the city desk, Rafferty thought. Joe'll know what to do. No, no. Joe would say you're drunk.

But this is the biggest story in the world, Rafferty's brain kept saying. It's the biggest story in the world and you just stand here.

'Listen, Alsop!' Rafferty yelled. 'You got a camera? Any kind of a camera. I *got* to have a camera!'

'Oh, sure,' Mr Alsop said. 'I got a fine camera. It's a box camera but it takes good pictures. I'll show you some I took of my chickens.'

'No, no! I don't want to see your pictures. I want the camera!'

Mr Alsop went into the parlour and Rafferty could see him fumbling around on top of the organ.

'Mrs Alsop!' Rafferty shouted. 'I've got to ask lots of questions!'

'Ask away,' Mrs Alsop said cheerily. 'They don't mind.'

But what could you ask people from space? You got their names. You got what they were here for: eggs. You got where they were from . . .

Mr Alsop's voice came from the parlour.

'Ethel, you seen my camera?'

Mrs Alsop sighed. 'No, I haven't. You put it away.'

'Only trouble is,' Mr Alsop said, 'haven't got any films for it.'

Suddenly the people from space turned their antennae toward each other for a second and apparently coming to a mutual agreement, got up and darted here and there about the room as quick as fireflies, so fast Rafferty could scarcely see them. They scuttered out the door and off toward the barn. All Rafferty could think was: 'My God, they're part bug!'

Rafferty rushed out the door, on toward the barn through the mud, screaming at the creatures to stop. But before he was half-way there the gleaming plastic contraption slid out of the barn and there was a slight hiss. The thing disappeared into the low hanging clouds.

All there was left for Rafferty to see was a steaming place in the mud and a little circle of burnt earth. Rafferty sat down in the mud, a hollow, empty feeling in his middle, with the knowledge that the greatest story in the world had gone off into the sky. No pictures, no evidence, no story. He dully went over in his mind the information he had:

'Mr and Mrs Man-Who-Bends-Iron . . .' It slowly dawned on Rafferty what that meant. Smith! Man-Who-Bends-Iron on an anvil. Of course that was Smith. . . . 'Mr and Mrs Smith visited at the Alfred Alsop place Sunday. They returned to their home in the system of Alpha Centauri with two crates of hatching eggs.'

Rafferty got to his feet and shook his head. He stood still in the mud and suddenly his eyes narrowed and you knew that Rafferty brain was working – that Rafferty brain that always came up with the story. He bolted for the house and burst in the back door.

'Alsop!' he yelled. 'Did those people pay for those eggs?'

Mr Alsop was standing on a chair in front of the china closet, still hunting for the camera.

'Oh, sure,' he said. 'In a way they did.'

'Let me see the money!' Rafferty demanded.

'Oh, not in money,' Mr Alsop said. 'They don't have any money. But when they were here six years ago they brought us some eggs of their own in trade.'

'Six years ago!' Rafferty moaned. Then he started. 'Eggs! What kind of eggs?'

Mr Alsop chuckled a little. 'Oh, I don't know,' he said. 'We called them star ducks. The eggs were star shaped. And you know we set them under a hen and the star points bothered the old hen something awful.'

Mr Alsop climbed down from the chair.

'Star ducks aren't much good, though. They look something like a little hippopotamus and something like a swallow. But they got six legs. Only two of them lived and we ate them for Thanksgiving.'

Rafferty's brain still worked, grasping for that single fragment of evidence that would make his city editor believe – that would make the world believe.

Rafferty leaned closer. 'Mr Alsop,' he almost whispered, 'you wouldn't know where the skeletons of the star ducks are?'

Mr Alsop looked puzzled. 'You mean the bones? We gave the bones to the dog. That was five years ago. Even the dog's dead now. I know where his bones are, though.'

Rafferty picked up his hat like a man in a daze.

'Thanks, Mr Alsop,' he said dully. 'Thanks.'

Rafferty stood on the porch and put on his hat. He pushed it back on his head. He stared up into the overcast; he stared until he felt dizzy like he was spiralling off into the mist, spiralling off the earth like a celestial barber pole.

Mr Alsop opened the door and came out, wiping the dust off a box camera with his sleeve.

'Oh, Mr Rafferty,' he said. 'I found the camera.'

Compassion Circuit
John Wyndham

By the time Janet had been five days in hospital she had become converted to the idea of a domestic robot. It had taken her two days to discover that Nurse James *was* a robot, one day to get over the surprise, and two more to realize what a comfort an attendant robot could be.

The conversion was a relief. Practically every house she visited had a domestic robot; it was the family's second or third most valuable possession – the women tended to rate it slightly higher than the car; the men, slightly lower. Janet had been perfectly well aware for some time that her friends regarded her as a nitwit or worse for wearing herself out with looking after a house which a robot would be able to keep spick and span with a few hours' work a day. She had also known that it irritated George to come home each evening to a wife who had tired herself out by unnecessary work. But the prejudice had been firmly set. It was not the diehard attitude of people who refused to be served by robot waiters, or driven by robot drivers (who, incidentally, were much safer), led by robot shop-guides, or see dresses modelled by robot mannequins. It was simply an uneasiness about them, and being left alone with one – and a disinclination to feel such an uneasiness in her own home.

She herself attributed the feeling largely to the conservatism of her own home which had used no house-robots. Other people, who had been brought up in homes run by robots, even the primitive types available a generation before, never seemed to have such a feeling at all. It irritated her to know that her husband thought she was *afraid* of them in a childish way. That, she had explained to George a number of times, was not so, and was not the point, either: what she did dislike was the idea of one intruding upon her personal, domestic life, which was what a house-robot was bound to do.

The robot who was called Nurse James was, then, the first with which she had ever been in close personal contact and she, or it, came as a revelation.

Janet told the doctor of her enlightenment, and he looked relieved. She also told George when he looked in in the afternoon: he was delighted. The two of them conferred before he left the hospital. 'Excellent,' said the doctor. 'To tell you the truth I was afraid we were up against a real neurosis there – and very inconveniently, too. Your wife can never have been strong, and in the last few years she's worn herself out running the house.'

'I know,' George agreed. 'I tried hard to persuade her during the first two years we were married, but it only led to trouble so I had to drop it. This is really a culmination – she was rather shaken when she found that the reason she'd have to come here was partly because there was no robot at home to look after her.'

'Well, there's one thing certain, she can't go on as she has been doing. If she tries to she'll be back here inside a couple of months,' the doctor told him.

'She won't now. She's really changed her mind,' George assured him. 'Part of the trouble was that she's never come across a really modern one, except in a superficial way. The newest that any of our friends has is ten years old at least, and most of them are older than that. She'd never contemplated the idea of anything as advanced as Nurse James. The question now is what pattern?'

The doctor thought a moment.

'Frankly, Mr Shand, your wife is going to need a lot of rest and looking after, I'm afraid. What I'd really recommend for her is the type they have here. It's something pretty new, this Nurse James model. A specially developed high-sensibility job with a quite novel contra-balanced compassion-protection circuit – a very tricky bit of work that – any direct order which a normal robot would obey at once is evaluated by the circuit, it is weighed against the benefit or harm to the patient, and unless it is beneficial, or at least harmless, to the patient, it is not obeyed. They've proved to be wonderful for nursing and looking after children – but there is a big demand for them, and I'm afraid they're pretty expensive.'

'How much?' asked George.

The doctor's round-figure price made him frown for a moment. Then he said:

'It'll make a hole, but, after all, it's mostly Janet's economies and simple living that's built up the savings. Where do I get one?'

'You don't. Not just like that,' the doctor told him. 'I shall have to throw a bit of weight about for a priority, but in the circumstances I shall get it, all right. Now, you go and fix up the details of appearance and so on with your wife. Let me know how she wants it, and I'll get busy.'

'A proper one,' said Janet. 'One that'll look right in a house, I mean. I couldn't do with one of those levers-and-plastic box things that stare at you with lenses. As it's got to look after the house, let's have it looking like a housemaid.'

'Or a houseman, if you like?'

She shook her head. 'No. It's going to have to look after me, too, so I think I'd rather it was a housemaid. It can have a black silk dress and a frilly white apron and a cap. And I'd like it blonde – a sort of darkish blonde – and about five feet ten, and nice to look at, but not *too* beautiful. I don't want to be jealous of it. . . .'

*

The doctor kept Janet ten days more in the hospital while the matter was settled. There had been luck in coming in for a cancelled order, but inevitably some delay while it was adapted to Janet's specification – also it had required the addition of standard domestic pseudo-memory patterns to suit it for housework.

It was delivered the day after she got back. Two severely functional robots carried the case up the front path, and inquired whether they should unpack it. Janet thought not, and told them to leave it in the outhouse.

When George got back he wanted to open it at once, but Janet shook her head.

'Supper first,' she decided. 'A robot doesn't mind waiting.'

Nevertheless it was a brief meal. When it was over, George carried the dishes out and stacked them in the sink.

'No more washing-up,' he said, with satisfaction.

He went out to borrow the next-door robot to help him carry the case in. Then he found his end of it more than he could lift, and had to borrow the robot from the house opposite, too. Presently the pair of them carried it in and laid it on the kitchen floor as if it were a featherweight, and went away again.

George got out the screwdriver and drew the six large screws that held the lid down. Inside there was a mass of shavings. He shoved them out, on to the floor.

Janet protested.

'What's the matter? We shan't have to clear up,' he said, happily.

There was an inner case of wood pulp, with a snowy layer of wadding under its lid. George rolled it up and pushed it out of the way, and there, ready dressed in black frock and white apron, lay the robot.

They regarded it for some seconds without speaking.

It was remarkably lifelike. For some reason it made Janet feel a little queer to realize that it was *her* robot – a trifle nervous, and, obscurely, a trifle guilty . . . .

'Sleeping beauty,' remarked George, reaching for the instruction book on its chest.

In point of fact the robot was not a beauty. Janet's preference had been observed. It was pleasant and nice-looking without being striking, but the details were good. The deep gold hair was quite enviable – although one knew that it was probably threads of plastic with waves that would never come out. The skin – another kind of plastic covering the carefully built-up contours – was distinguishable from real skin only by its perfection.

Janet knelt down beside the box, and ventured a forefinger to touch the flawless complexion. It was quite, quite cold.

She sat back on her heels, looking at it. Just a big doll, she told herself; a contraption, a very wonderful contraption of metal, plastic, and electronic circuits, but still a contraption, and made to look as it did simply because people, including herself, would find it harsh or grotesque if it should look any other way . . . . And yet, to have it looking as it did was a bit disturbing, too. For one thing, you couldn't go on thinking of it as 'it' any more; whether you liked it or not, your mind thought of it as 'her'. As 'her' it would have to have a name; and, with a name, it would become still more of a person.

'"A battery-driven model",' George read out, '"will normally require to be fitted with a new battery every four days. Other models, however, are designed to conduct their own regeneration from the mains as and when necessary." Let's have her out.'

He put his hands under the robot's shoulders, and tried to lift it.

'Phew!' he said. 'Must be about three times my weight.'
He had another try. 'Hell,' he said, and referred to the
book again.

'"The control switches are situated at the back, slightly
above the waistline." All right, maybe we can roll her over.'

With an effort he succeeded in getting the figure on to
its side and began to undo the buttons at the back of her
dress. Janet suddenly felt that to be an indelicacy.

'I'll do it,' she said.

Her husband glanced at her.

'All right. It's yours,' he told her.

'She can't be just "it". I'm going to call her Hester.'

'All right, again,' he agreed.

Janet undid the buttons and fumbled about inside
the dress.

'I can't find a knob, or anything,' she said.

'Apparently there's a small panel that opens,' he told her.

'Oh, no!' she said, in a slightly shocked tone.

He regarded her again.

'Darling, she's just a robot; a mechanism.'

'I know,' said Janet, shortly. She felt about again,
discovered the panel, and opened it.

'You give the upper knob a half-turn to the right and
then close the panel to complete the circuit,' instructed
George, from the book.

Janet did so, and then sat swiftly back on her heels
again, watching.

The robot stirred and turned. It sat up, then it got to its
feet. It stood before them, looking the very pattern of a
stage parlourmaid.

'Good day, madam,' it said. 'Good day, sir. I shall be
happy to serve you.'

'Thank you, Hester,' Janet said, as she leaned back against
the cushion placed behind her. Not that it was necessary

to thank a robot, but she had a theory that if you did not practise politeness with robots you soon forgot it with other people.

And, anyway, Hester was no ordinary robot. She was not even dressed as a parlourmaid any more. In four months she had become a friend, a tireless, attentive friend. From the first Janet had found it difficult to believe that she was only a mechanism, and as the days passed she had become more and more of a person. The fact that she consumed electricity instead of food came to seem little more than a foible. The time she couldn't stop walking in a circle, and the other time when something went wrong with her vision so that she did everything a foot to the right of where she ought to have been doing it, these things were just indispositions such as anyone might have, and the robot-mechanic who came to adjust her paid his call much like any other doctor. Hester was not only a person; she was preferable company to many.

'I suppose,' said Janet, settling back in her chair, 'that you must think me a poor, weak thing?'

What one must not expect from Hester was euphemism.

'Yes,' she said, directly. But then she added: 'I think all humans are poor, weak things. It is the way they are made. One must be sorry for them.'

Janet had long ago given up thinking things like: 'That'll be the compassion-circuit speaking', or trying to imagine the computing, selecting, associating, and shunting that must be going on to produce such a remark. She took it as she might from – well, say, a foreigner. She said:

'Compared with robots we must seem so, I suppose. You are so strong and untiring, Hester. If you knew how I envy you that . . . .'

Hester said, matter-of-factly:

'We were designed: you were just accidental. It is your misfortune, not your fault.'

'You'd rather be you than me?' asked Janet.

'Certainly,' Hester told her. 'We are stronger. We don't have to have frequent sleep to recuperate. We don't have to carry an unreliable chemical factory inside us. We don't have to grow old and deteriorate. Human beings are so clumsy and fragile and so often unwell because something is not working properly. If anything goes wrong with us, or is broken, it doesn't hurt and is easily replaced. And you have all kinds of words like pain, and suffering, and unhappiness, and weariness that we have to be taught to understand, and they don't seem to us to be useful things to have. I feel very sorry that you must have these things and be so uncertain and so fragile. It disturbs my compassion-circuit.'

'Uncertain and fragile,' Janet repeated. 'Yes, that's how I feel.'

'Humans have to live so precariously,' Hester went on. 'If my arm or leg should be crushed I can have a new one in a few minutes, but a human would have agony for a long time, and not even a new limb at the end of it – just a faulty one, if he is lucky. That isn't as bad as it used to be because in designing us you learned how to make good arms and legs, much stronger and better than the old ones. People would be much more sensible to have a weak arm or leg replaced at once, but they don't seem to want to if they can possibly keep the old ones.'

'You mean they can be grafted on? I didn't know that,' Janet said. 'I wish it were only arms or legs that's wrong with me. I don't think I would hesitate . . . .' She sighed. 'The doctor wasn't encouraging this morning, Hester. You heard what he said? I've been losing ground: must rest more. I don't believe he does expect me to get any stronger. He was just trying to cheer me up before . . . . He had a funny sort of look after he'd examined me . . . . But all he said was rest.

What's the good of being alive if it's only rest – rest – rest . . . ? And there's poor George. What sort of a life is it for him, and he's so patient with me, so sweet . . . I'd rather anything than go on feebly like this. I'd sooner die . . . .'

Janet went on talking, more to herself than to the patient Hester standing by. She talked herself into tears. Then, presently, she looked up.

'Oh, Hester, if you were human I couldn't bear it; I think I'd hate you for being so strong and so well – but I don't, Hester. You're so kind and so patient when I'm silly, like this. I believe you'd cry with me to keep me company if you could.'

'I would if I could,' the robot agreed. 'My compassion-circuit –'

'Oh, *no!*' Janet protested. 'It can't be just that. You've a heart somewhere, Hester. You must have.'

'I expect it is more reliable than a heart,' said Hester.

She stepped a little closer, stooped down, and lifted Janet up as if she weighed nothing at all.

'You've tired yourself out, Janet, dear,' she told her. 'I'll take you upstairs; you'll be able to sleep a little before he gets back.'

Janet could feel the robot's arms cold through her dress, but the coldness did not trouble her any more, she was aware only that they were strong, protecting arms around her. She said:

'Oh, Hester, you are such a comfort, you *know* what I ought to do.' She paused, then she added miserably: 'I know what he thinks – the doctor, I mean. I could see it. He just thinks I'm going to go on getting weaker and weaker until one day I'll fade away and die . . . . I said I'd sooner die . . . but I wouldn't, Hester. I don't want to die . . . .'

The robot rocked her a little, as if she were a child.

'There, there, dear. It's not as bad as that – nothing like,' she told her. 'You mustn't think about dying. And you mustn't cry any more, it's not good for you, you know. Besides, you don't want him to see you've been crying.'

'I'll try not to,' agreed Janet obediently, as Hester carried her out of the room and up the stairs.

The hospital reception-robot looked up from the desk.

'My wife,' George said, 'I rang you up about an hour ago.'

The robot's face took on an impeccable expression of professional sympathy.

'Yes, Mr Shand. I'm afraid it has been a shock for you, but as I told you, your house-robot did quite the right thing to send her here at once.'

'I've tried to get on to her own doctor, but he's away,' George told her.

'You don't need to worry about that, Mr Shand. She has been examined, and we have had all her records sent over from the hospital she was in before. The operation has been provisionally fixed for tomorrow, but of course we shall need your consent.'

George hesitated. 'May I see the doctor in charge of her?'

'He isn't in the hospital at the moment, I'm afraid.'

'Is it – absolutely necessary?' George asked after a pause.

The robot looked at him steadily, and nodded.

'She must have been growing steadily weaker for some months now,' she said.

George nodded.

'The only alternative is that she will grow weaker still, and have more pain before the end,' she told him.

George stared at the wall blankly for some seconds.

'I see,' he said bleakly.

He picked up a pen in a shaky hand and signed the form that she put before him. He gazed at it a while without seeing it.

'She'll – she'll have – a good chance?' he asked.

'Yes,' the robot told him. 'There is never complete absence of risk, of course, but she has a better than seventy-per-cent likelihood of complete success.'

George sighed, and nodded.

'I'd like to see her,' he said.

The robot pressed a bell-push.

'You may *see* her,' she said. 'But I must ask you not to disturb her. She's asleep now, and it's better for her not to be woken.'

George had to be satisfied with that, but he left the hospital feeling a little better for the sight of the quiet smile on Janet's lips as she slept.

The hospital called him at the office the following afternoon. They were reassuring. The operation appeared to have been a complete success. Everyone was quite confident of the outcome. There was no need to worry. The doctors were perfectly satisfied. No, it would not be wise to allow any visitors for a few days yet. But there was nothing to worry about. Nothing at all.

George rang up each day just before he left, in the hope that he would be allowed a visit. The hospital was kindly and heartening, but adamant about visits. And then, on the fifth day, they suddenly told him she had left on her way home. George was staggered: he had been prepared to find it a matter of weeks. He dashed out, bought a bunch of roses, and left half a dozen traffic regulations in fragments behind him.

'Where is she?' he demanded of Hester as she opened the door.

'She's in bed. I thought it might be better if –' Hester began, but he lost the rest of the sentence as he bounded up the stairs.

Janet was lying in the bed. Only her head was visible, cut off by the line of the sheet and a bandage round her neck. George put the flowers down on the bedside table. He stooped over Janet and kissed her gently. She looked up at him from anxious eyes.

'Oh, George dear. Has she told you?'

'Has who told me what?' he asked, sitting down on the side of the bed.

'Hester. She said she would. Oh, George, I didn't mean it, at least I don't think I meant it . . . . She sent me, George. I was so weak and wretched. I wanted to be strong. I don't think I really understood. Hester said –'

'Take it easy, darling. Take it easy,' George suggested with a smile. 'What on earth's all this about?'

He felt under the bedclothes and found her hand.

'But, George –' she began. He interrupted her.

'I say, darling, your hand's dreadfully cold. It's almost like –' His fingers slid further up her arm. His eyes widened at her, incredulously. He jumped up suddenly from the bed and flung back the covers. He put his hand on the thin nightdress, over her heart – and then snatched it away as if he had been stung.

'God! – *NO!* –' he said, staring at her.

'But George. George, darling –' said Janet's head on the pillows.

'*NO! – NO!*' cried George, almost in a shriek.

He turned and ran blindly from the room.

In the darkness on the landing he missed the top step of the stairs, and went headlong down the whole flight.

Hester found him lying in a huddle in the hall. She bent down and gently explored the damage. The extent of it, and the fragility of the frame that had suffered it disturbed her compassion-circuit very greatly. She did not try to move him, but went to the telephone and dialled.

'Emergency?' she asked, and gave the name and address. 'Yes, at once,' she told them. 'There may not be a lot of time. Several compound fractures, and I think his back is broken, poor man. No. There appears to be no damage to his head. Yes, much better. He'd be crippled for life, even if he did get over it . . . . Yes, better send the form of consent with the ambulance so that it can be signed at once . . . . Oh, yes, that'll be quite all right. His wife will sign it.'

The Stolen Bacillus

H. G. Wells

'This again,' said the Bacteriologist, slipping a glass slide under the microscope, 'is a preparation of the celebrated Bacillus of cholera – the cholera germ.'

The pale-faced man peered down the microscope. He was evidently not accustomed to that kind of thing, and held a limp white hand over his disengaged eye. 'I see very little,' he said.

'Touch this screw,' said the Bacteriologist; 'perhaps the microscope is out of focus for you. Eyes vary so much. Just the fraction of a turn this way or that.'

'Ah! now I see,' said the visitor. 'Not so very much to see after all. Little streaks and shreds of pink. And yet those little particles, those mere atomies, might multiply and devastate a city! Wonderful!'

He stood up, and releasing the glass slip from the microscope, held it in his hand towards the window. 'Scarcely visible,' he said, scrutinizing the preparation. He hesitated. 'Are these – alive? Are they dangerous now?'

'Those have been stained and killed,' said the Bacteriologist. 'I wish, for my own part, we could kill and stain every one of them in the universe.'

'I suppose,' the pale man said with a slight smile, 'that you scarcely care to have such things about you in the living – in the active state?'

'On the contrary, we are obliged to,' said the Bacteriologist. 'Here, for instance –' He walked across the room and took up one of several sealed tubes. 'Here is the living thing. This is a cultivation of the actual living disease bacteria.' He hesitated. 'Bottled cholera, so to speak.'

A slight gleam of satisfaction appeared momentarily in the face of the pale man. 'It's a deadly thing to have in your possession,' he said, devouring the little tube with his eyes. The Bacteriologist watched the **morbid** pleasure in his visitor's expression. This man, who had visited him that afternoon with a note of introduction from an old friend, interested him from the very contrast of their dispositions. The lank black hair and deep grey eyes, the haggard expression and nervous manner, the fitful yet keen interest of his visitor were a novel change from the **phlegmatic** deliberations of the ordinary scientific worker with whom the Bacteriologist chiefly associated. It was perhaps natural, with a hearer evidently so impressionable to the lethal nature of his topic, to take the most effective aspect of the matter.

He held the tube in his hand thoughtfully. 'Yes, here is the pestilence imprisoned. Only break such a little tube as this into a supply of drinking-water, say to these minute particles of life that one must needs stain and examine with the highest powers of the microscope even to see, and that one can neither smell nor taste – say to them, 'Go forth, increase and multiply, and replenish the cisterns,' and death – mysterious, untraceable death, death swift and terrible, death full of pain and indignity – would be released upon this city, and go hither and thither seeking his victims. Here he would take the husband from the wife, here the child from its mother, here the statesman from his duty, and here the toiler from his trouble. He would follow the water-mains, creeping along streets, picking out and punishing a house here and a house there where they did not boil their drinking-water, creeping into the wells of the mineral-water makers, getting washed into salad, and lying dormant in

---

morbid: unhealthy
phlegmatic: unemotional

ices. He would wait ready to be drunk in the horse-troughs, and by unwary children in the public fountains. He would soak into the soil, to reappear in springs and wells at a thousand unexpected places. Once start him at the water supply, and before we could ring him in, and catch him again, he would have **decimated** the metropolis.'

He stopped abruptly. He had been told rhetoric was his weakness.

'But he is quite safe here, you know – quite safe.'

The pale-faced man nodded. His eyes shone. He cleared his throat. 'These Anarchist – rascals,' said he, 'are fools, blind fools – to use bombs when this kind of thing is attainable. I think –'

A gentle rap, a mere light touch of the finger-nails was heard at the door. The Bacteriologist opened it. 'Just a minute, dear,' whispered his wife.

When he re-entered the laboratory his visitor was looking at his watch. 'I had no idea I had wasted an hour of your time,' he said. 'Twelve minutes to four. I ought to have left here by half-past three. But your things were really too interesting. No, positively I cannot stop a moment longer. I have an engagement at four.'

He passed out of the room reiterating his thanks, and the Bacteriologist accompanied him to the door, and then returned thoughtfully along the passage to his laboratory. He was musing on the **ethnology** of his visitor. Certainly the man was not a Teutonic type nor a common Latin one. 'A morbid product, anyhow, I am afraid,' said the Bacteriologist to himself. 'How he gloated on those cultivations of disease-germs!' A disturbing thought struck him. He turned to the bench by the vapour-bath,

---

decimate: kill one person in ten
ethnology: ethnic origin

and then very quickly to his writing-table. Then he felt hastily in his pockets, and then rushed to the door. 'I may have put it down on the hall table,' he said.

'Minnie!' he shouted hoarsely in the hall.

'Yes, dear,' came a remote voice.

'Had I anything in my hand when I spoke to you, dear, just now?'

Pause.

'Nothing, dear, because I remember –'

'Blue ruin!' cried the Bacteriologist, and **incontinently** ran to the front door and down the steps of his house to the street.

Minnie, hearing the door slam violently, ran in alarm to the window. Down the street a slender man was getting into a cab. The Bacteriologist, hatless, and in his carpet slippers, was running and gesticulating wildly towards this group. One slipper came off, but he did not wait for it. 'He has gone *mad!*' said Minnie; 'it's that horrid science of his'; and, opening the window, would have called after him. The slender man, suddenly glancing round, seemed struck with the same idea of mental disorder. He pointed hastily to the Bacteriologist, said something to the cabman, the apron of the cab slammed, the whip swished, the horse's feet clattered, and in a moment cab, and Bacteriologist hotly in pursuit, had receded up the vista of the roadway and disappeared round the corner.

Minnie remained straining out of the window for a minute. Then she drew her head back into the room again. She was dumbfounded. 'Of course he is eccentric,' she meditated. 'But running about London – in the height of the season, too – in his socks!' A happy thought struck her. She hastily put her bonnet on, seized his shoes, went

---

incontinently: in an uncontrolled rush

into the hall, took down his hat and light overcoat from the pegs, emerged upon the doorstep, and hailed a cab that opportunely crawled by. 'Drive me up the road and round Havelock Crescent, and see if we can find a gentleman running about in a velveteen coat and no hat.'

'Velveteen coat, ma'am, and no 'at. Very good, ma'am.' And the cabman whipped up at once in the most matter-of-fact way, as if he drove to this address every day in his life.

Some few minutes later the little group of cabmen and loafers that collects round the cabmen's shelter at Haverstock Hill were startled by the passing of a cab with a ginger-coloured screw of a horse, driven furiously.

They were silent as it went by, and then as it receded – 'That's 'Arry 'Icks. Wot's *he* got?' said the stout gentleman known as Old Tootles.

'He's a-using his whip, he is, *to* rights,' said the ostler boy.

'Hullo!' said poor old Tommy Byles; 'here's another bloomin' loonatic. Blowed if there ain't.'

'It's old George,' said old Tootles, 'and he's drivin' a loonatic, *as* you say. Ain't he a-clawin' out of the keb? Wonder if he's after 'Arry 'Icks?'

The group round the cabmen's shelter became animated. Chorus: 'Go it, George!' 'It's a race!' 'You'll ketch 'em!' 'Whip up!'

'She's a goer, she is!' said the ostler boy.

'Strike me giddy!' cried old Tootles. 'Here! *I'm* a-goin' to begin in a minute. Here's another comin'. If all the kebs in Hampstead ain't gone mad this morning!'

'It's a **fieldmale** this time,' said the ostler boy.

'She's a followin' *him*,' said old Tootles. 'Usually the other way about.'

---

fieldmale: woman (female)

'What's she got in her 'and?'

'Looks like a 'igh 'at.'

'What a bloomin' lark it is! Three to one on old George,' said the ostler boy. 'Next!'

Minnie went by in a perfect roar of applause. She did not like it but she felt that she was doing her duty, and whirled on down Haverstock Hill and Camden Town High Street with her eyes ever intent on the animated back view of old George, who was driving her vagrant husband so incomprehensively away from her.

The man in the foremost cab sat crouched in the corner, his arms tightly folded, and the little tube that contained such vast possibilities of destruction gripped in his hand. His mood was a singular mixture of fear and exultation. Chiefly he was afraid of being caught before he could accomplish his purpose, but behind this was a vaguer but larger fear of the awfulness of his crime. But his exultation far exceeded his fear. No Anarchist before him had ever approached this conception of his. Ravachol, Vaillant, all those distinguished persons whose fame he had envied dwindled into insignificance beside him. He had only to make sure of the water supply, and break the little tube into a reservoir. How brilliantly he had planned it, forged the letter of introduction and got into the laboratory, and how brilliantly he had seized his opportunity! The world should hear of him at last. All those people who had sneered at him, neglected him, preferred other people to him, found his company undesirable, should consider him at last. Death, death, death! They had always treated him as a man of no importance. All the world had been in a conspiracy to keep him under. He would teach them yet what it is to isolate a man. What was this familiar street? Great Saint Andrew's Street, of course! How fared the chase! He craned out of the cab. The Bacteriologist was scarcely fifty yards behind. That was bad. He would be caught and stopped yet. He felt in his pocket for money, and found half-a-sovereign. This he thrust up through the trap in the top of the cab into the man's face. 'More,' he shouted, 'if only we get away.'

The money was snatched out of his hand. 'Right you are,' said the cabman, and the trap slammed, and the lash lay along the glistening side of the horse. The cab swayed, and the Anarchist, half-standing under the trap, put the hand containing the little glass tube upon the apron to preserve his balance. He felt the brittle thing crack, and the broken half of it rang upon the floor of the cab. He fell back into the seat with a curse, and stared dismally at the two or three drops of moisture on the apron.

He shuddered.

'Well! I suppose I shall be the first. *Phew!* Anyhow, I shall be a Martyr. That's something. But it is a filthy death, nevertheless. I wonder if it hurts as much as they say.'

Presently a thought occurred to him – he groped between his feet. A little drop was still in the broken end of the tube, and he drank that to make sure. It was better to make sure. At any rate, he would not fail.

Then it dawned upon him that there was no further need to escape the Bacteriologist. In Wellington Street he told the cabman to stop, and got out. He slipped on the step, and his head felt queer. It was rapid stuff this cholera poison. He waved his cabman out of existence, so to speak, and stood on the pavement with his arm folded upon his breast awaiting the arrival of the Bacteriologist. There was something tragic in his pose. The sense of imminent death gave him a certain dignity. He greeted his pursuer with a defiant laugh.

'*Vive l'Anarchie!* You are too late, my friend. I have drunk it. The cholera is abroad!'

The Bacteriologist from his cab beamed curiously at him through his spectacles. 'You have drunk it! An Anarchist! I see now.' He was about to say something more, and then checked himself. A smile hung in the corner of his mouth. He opened the apron of his cab as if to descend, at which the Anarchist waved him a dramatic farewell and strode off towards Waterloo Bridge, carefully jostling his infected body against as many people as possible. The Bacteriologist was so preoccupied with the vision of him that he scarcely manifested the slightest surprise at the appearance of Minnie upon the pavement with his hat and shoes and overcoat. 'Very good of you to bring my things,' he said, and remained lost in contemplation of the receding figure of the Anarchist.

'You had better get in,' he said, still staring. Minnie felt absolutely convinced now that he was mad, and directed the cabman home on her own responsibility. 'Put on my shoes? Certainly, dear,' said he, as the cab began to turn, and hid the strutting black figure, now small in the distance, from his eyes. Then suddenly something grotesque struck him, and he laughed. Then he remarked, 'It is really very serious, though.'

'You see, that man came to my house to see me, and he is an Anarchist. No – don't faint, or I cannot possibly tell you the rest. And I wanted to astonish him, not knowing he was an Anarchist, and took up a cultivation of that new species of Bacterium I was telling you of, that infest, and I think cause, the blue patches upon various monkeys; and like a fool, I said it was Asiatic cholera. And he ran away with it to poison the water of London, and he certainly might have made things look blue for this civilized city. And now he has swallowed it. Of course, I cannot say what will happen, but you know it turned that kitten blue, and the three puppies – in patches, and the sparrow – bright blue. But the bother is, I shall have all the trouble and expense of preparing some more.

'Put on my coat on this hot day! Why? Because we might meet Mrs Jabber. My dear, Mrs Jabber is not a draught. But why should I wear a coat on a hot day because of Mrs – ? Oh, *very* well.'

Science Fiction: Activities

Reading science fiction

1 a) Look at *A Gnaw of Rats*. Imagine you are an enthusiastic Demolition-rat, describing your role to an ordinary rat. Explain in detail to your partner what the master plan is, and what your role is, giving a reason for the whole plan.

b) *A Gnaw of Rats* is set in the future, but the setting is very familiar. What do you think the author might be saying about the society of today in his story?

2 a) *The Star Ducks* is a story which shows how outer space and the prospect of different life forms are of great attraction and also concern to us. Answer the following questions about the Alsops' visitors and the characters' reactions to them.

　　i)　What would you expect to concern the Alsops about their visitors?

　　ii)　How do the Alsops actually react to them?

　　iii)　What does Rafferty feel about the Alsops when he first arrives at their house? Why?

　　iv)　How does Rafferty react to the visitors?

b) Why do you think that the author shows two such different reactions to the aliens? Here are some possible reasons:

- to make the story amusing
- to show that the Alsops' attitude to – and simple acceptance of – life is better

- to show that you cannot always have what you want
- to show the difference between Rafferty's selfishness and the Alsops' generosity
- to show the difference between country and city life.

Find an example from the text to support each of these reasons. Then say which one(s) you find the most convincing and explain why.

3 Look at *Compassion Circuit*. Which of the following elements of science fiction are evident in this story? Give at least **one** example from the text of each feature you decide on.
- told in the third person
- use of new technology
- use of unfamiliar creatures, people or objects
- set in the future
- set in an unusual place
- the main character confronts something unusual
- other worlds, societies and experiences are suggested or shown.

4 H. G. Wells' Bacteriologist in *The Stolen Bacillus* is an interesting character. Think about each of the following examples of his behaviour, then write down what each one tells you about his character:
- his deliberate lie about the bacteria being cholera, a dangerous disease
- his dramatic description of the deadly bacteria
- his forgetfulness with the test tube and his clothes
- his relationship with his wife

- his reaction when he finds out the thief has drunk the contents of the test tube.

Original writing

1 Imagine you are a person living at the time the rats start to take over in *A Gnaw of Rats*. Write an account of what happened, from the first case of the plague to the point when you decide to escape to the countryside.

2 Imagine you are Rafferty in *The Star Ducks*. After you get back from the Alsops', you decide to write an account of your experience for your newspaper, even though you have no proof. Write the story for the front page of the newspaper. Remember to include details of:

- what happened
- where it happened
- when it happened
- who was there
- your own reaction to, and opinion of the event.

You could use quotes from the Alsops and any other details you think are important.

3 Write a story of about 300 words in which an alien comes to earth. Remember to include details of:

- what the alien looks like
- who meets the alien and how they react to it
- how the alien reacts to earth
- what the alien wants
- how the alien leaves
- whether anyone believes in the alien's visit.

4 Think of an invention or discovery such as:
- a time/weather machine
- a device to predict the future
- a potion to stop you growing any older
- a way to produce identical people.

Write **one** paragraph describing the invention. Then write **two** further paragraphs in which you imagine what might go wrong if the invention were developed in a thoughtless way – for example, for personal power, political control or to harm others. Include details of the long-term effects on people, society and the environment. How might it change the way we live?

Section 4
Crime and Mystery

Everybody is fascinated by crime and mystery stories. They give us the chance to search for clues and piece together the solution – even if we sometimes get it wrong and are surprised by the author's 'twist' at the end.

A mystery story may not even end in a neat solution. The source of the mystery may be something far back in the past. You then have to examine the author's clues and provide your own explanation for mysterious events. You may be left still speculating about the solution at the end. This type of story allows different people to draw different conclusions from the same evidence, depending on their own point of view.

Crime stories often show society threatened by disorder but end with the restoration of order and the triumph of justice, thereby making the reader feel secure and satisfied. Other stories may unexpectedly ask us to side with the criminal, and pose the question of whether some crimes may be justified.

Some of the stories in this selection are about crime while others are mystery stories. All provide clues for the alert reader and offer various surprises along the way.

The Hitch-hiker
Roald Dahl

I had a new car. It was an exciting toy, a big B.M.W. 3.3 Li, which means 3.3 litre, long wheelbase, fuel injection. It had a top speed of 129 m.p.h. and terrific acceleration. The body was pale blue. The seats inside were darker blue and they were made of leather, genuine soft leather of the finest quality. The windows were electrically operated and so was the sun-roof. The radio aerial popped up when I switched on the radio, and disappeared when I switched it off. The powerful engine growled and grunted impatiently at slow speeds, but at sixty miles an hour the growling stopped and the motor began to purr with pleasure.

I was driving up to London by myself. It was a lovely June day. They were haymaking in the fields and there were buttercups along both sides of the road. I was whispering along at seventy miles an hour, leaning back comfortably in my seat, with no more than a couple of fingers resting lightly on the wheel to keep her steady. Ahead of me I saw a man thumbing a lift. I touched the footbrake and brought the car to a stop beside him. I always stopped for hitch-hikers. I knew just how it used to feel to be standing on the side of a country road watching the cars go by. I hated the drivers for pretending they didn't see me, especially the ones in big cars with three empty seats. The large expensive cars seldom stopped. It was always the smaller ones that offered you a lift, or the old rusty ones, or the ones that were already crammed full of children and the driver would say, 'I think we can squeeze in one more'.

The hitch-hiker poked his head through the open window and said, 'Going to London, guv'nor?'

'Yes,' I said. 'Jump in.'

He got in and I drove on.

He was a small ratty-faced man with grey teeth. His eyes were dark and quick and clever, like a rat's eyes, and his ears were slightly pointed at the top. He had a cloth cap on his head and he was wearing a greyish-coloured jacket with enormous pockets. The grey jacket, together with the quick eyes and the pointed ears, made him look more than anything like some sort of a huge human rat.

'What part of London are you headed for?' I asked him.

'I'm goin' right through London and out the other side,' he said. 'I'm goin' to Epsom, for the races. It's Derby Day today.'

'So it is,' I said. 'I wish I were going with you. I love betting on horses.'

'I never bet on horses,' he said. 'I don't even watch 'em run. That's a stupid silly business.'

'Then why do you go?' I asked.

He didn't seem to like that question. His little ratty face went absolutely blank and he sat there staring straight ahead at the road, saying nothing.

'I expect you help to work the betting machines or something like that,' I said.

'That's even sillier,' he answered. 'There's no fun working them lousy machines and selling tickets to mugs. Any fool could do that.'

There was a long silence. I decided not to question him any more. I remembered how irritated I used to get in my hitch-hiking days when drivers kept asking *me* questions. Where are you going? Why are you going there? What's your job? Are you married? Do you have a girl-friend? What's her name? How old are you? And so on and so forth. I used to hate it.

'I'm sorry,' I said. 'It's none of my business what you do. The trouble is, I'm a writer, and most writers are terrible nosy parkers.'

'You write books?' he asked.

'Yes.'

'Writin' books is okay,' he said. 'It's what I call a skilled trade. I'm in a skilled trade too. The folks I despise is them that spend all their lives doin' crummy old routine jobs with no skill in 'em at all. You see what I mean?'

'Yes.'

'The secret of life,' he said, 'is to become very very good at somethin' that's very very 'ard to do.'

'Like you,' I said.

'Exactly. You and me both.'

'What makes you think that *I'm* any good at my job?' I asked. 'There's an awful lot of bad writers around.'

'You wouldn't be drivin' about in a car like this if you weren't no good at it,' he answered. 'It must've cost a tidy packet, this little job.'

'It wasn't cheap.'

'What can she do flat out?' he asked.

'One hundred and twenty-nine miles an hour,' I told him.

'I'll bet she won't do it.'

'I'll bet she will.'

'All car makers is liars,' he said. 'You can buy any car you like and it'll never do what the makers say it will in the ads.'

'This one will.'

'Open 'er up then and prove it,' he said. 'Go on, guv'nor, open 'er right up and let's see what she'll do.'

There is a roundabout at Chalfont St Peter and immediately beyond it there's a long straight section of dual carriageway. We came out of the roundabout on to the carriageway and I pressed my foot hard down on the accelerator. The big car leaped forward as though she'd been stung. In ten seconds or so, we were doing ninety.

'Lovely!' he cried. 'Beautiful! Keep goin'!'

I had the accelerator jammed right down against the floor and I held it there.

'One hundred!' he shouted . . . 'A hundred and five! . . . A hundred and ten! . . . A hundred and fifteen! Go on! Don't slack off!'

I was in the outside lane and we flashed past several cars as though they were standing still – a green Mini, a big cream-coloured Citroën, a white Land-Rover, a huge truck with a container on the back, an orange-coloured Volkswagen Minibus . . .

'A hundred and twenty!' my passenger shouted, jumping up and down. 'Go on! Go on! Get 'er up to one-two-nine!'

At that moment, I heard the scream of a police siren. It was so loud it seemed to be right inside the car, and then a policeman on a motor-cycle loomed up alongside us on the inside lane and went past us and raised a hand for us to stop.

'Oh, my sainted aunt!' I said. 'That's torn it!'

The policeman must have been doing about a hundred and thirty when he passed us, and he took plenty of time slowing down. Finally, he pulled into the side of the road and I pulled in behind him. 'I didn't know police motor-cycles could go as fast as that,' I said rather lamely.

'That one can,' my passenger said. 'It's the same make as yours. It's a B.M.W. R90S. Fastest bike on the road. That's what they're usin' nowadays.'

The policeman got off his motor-cycle and leaned the machine sideways on to its prop stand. Then he took off his gloves and placed them carefully on the seat. He was in no hurry now. He had us where he wanted us and he knew it.

'This is real trouble,' I said. 'I don't like it one bit.'

'Don't talk to 'im any more than is necessary, you understand,' my companion said. 'Just sit tight and keep mum.'

Like an executioner approaching his victim, the policeman came strolling slowly toward us. He was a big meaty man with a belly, and his blue breeches were skin-tight around his enormous thighs. His goggles were pulled up on to the helmet, showing a smouldering red face with wide cheeks.

We sat there like guilty schoolboys, waiting for him to arrive.

'Watch out for this man,' my passenger whispered. ''Ee looks mean as the devil.'

The policeman came round to my open window and placed one meaty hand on the sill. 'What's the hurry?' he said.

'No hurry, officer,' I answered.

'Perhaps there's a woman in the back having a baby and you're rushing her to hospital? Is that it?'

'No, officer.'

'Or perhaps your house is on fire and you're dashing home to rescue the family from upstairs?' His voice was dangerously soft and mocking.

'My house isn't on fire, officer.'

'In that case,' he said, 'you've got yourself into a nasty mess, haven't you? Do you know what the speed limit is in this country?'

'Seventy,' I said.

'And do you mind telling me exactly what speed you were doing just now?'

I shrugged and didn't say anything.

When he spoke next, he raised his voice so loud that I jumped. '*One hundred and twenty miles per hour!*' he barked. 'That's *fifty* miles an hour over the limit!'

He turned his head and spat out a big gob of spit. It landed on the wing of my car and started sliding down over my beautiful blue paint. Then he turned back again and stared hard at my passenger. 'And who are you?' he asked sharply.

'He's a hitch-hiker,' I said. 'I'm giving him a lift.'

'I didn't ask you,' he said. 'I asked him.'

"Ave I done somethin' wrong?' my passenger asked. His voice was as soft and oily as haircream.

'That's more than likely,' the policeman answered. 'Anyway, you're a witness. I'll deal with you in a minute. Driving-licence,' he snapped, holding out his hand.

I gave him my driving-licence.

He unbuttoned the left-hand breast-pocket of his tunic and brought out the dreaded book of tickets. Carefully, he copied the name and address from my licence. Then he gave it back to me. He strolled round to the front of the car and read the number from the number-plate and wrote that down as well. He filled in the date, the time and the details of my offence. Then he tore out the top copy of the ticket. But before handing it to me, he checked that all the information had come through clearly on his own carbon copy. Finally, he replaced the book in his tunic pocket and fastened the button.

'Now you,' he said to my passenger, and he walked around to the other side of the car. From the other breast-pocket he produced a small black notebook. 'Name?' he snapped.

'Michael Fish,' my passenger said.

'Address?'

'Fourteen, Windsor Lane, Luton.'

'Show me something to prove this is your real name and address', the policeman said.

My passenger fished in his pockets and came out with a driving-licence of his own. The policeman checked the name and address and handed it back to him. 'What's your job?' he asked sharply.

'I'm an 'od carrier.'

'A *what*?'

'An 'od carrier.'

'Spell it.'

'H-O-D C-A- . . .'

'That'll do. And what's a hod carrier, may I ask?'

'An 'od carrier, officer, is a person 'oo carries the cement up the ladder to the bricklayer. And the 'od is what 'ee carries it in. It's got a long 'andle, and on the top you've got two bits of wood set at an angle . . .'

'All right, all right. Who's your employer?'

'Don't 'ave one. I'm unemployed.'

The policeman wrote all this down in the black notebook. Then he returned the book to its pocket and did up the button.

'When I get back to the station I'm going to do a little checking up on you,' he said to my passenger.

'Me? What've I done wrong?' the rat-faced man asked.

'I don't like your face, that's all,' the policeman said. 'And we just might have a picture of it somewhere in our files.' He strolled round the car and returned to my window.

'I suppose you know you're in serious trouble,' he said to me.

'Yes, officer.'

'You won't be driving this fancy car of yours again for a very long time, not after *we've* finished with you. You won't be driving *any* car again, come to that, for several years. And a good thing, too. I hope they lock you up for a spell into the bargain.'

'You mean prison?' I asked, alarmed.

'Absolutely,' he said, smacking his lips. 'In the clink. Behind the bars. Along with all the other criminals who break the law. *And* a hefty fine into the bargain. Nobody will be more pleased about that than me. I'll see you in court, both of you. You'll be getting a summons to appear.'

He turned away and walked over to his motor-cycle. He flipped the prop stand back into position with his foot and swung his leg over the saddle. Then he kicked the starter and roared off up the road out of sight.

'Phew!' I gasped. 'That's done it.'

'We was caught,' my passenger said. 'We was caught good and proper.'

'I was caught, you mean.'

'That's right,' he said. 'What you goin' to do now, guv'nor?'

'I'm going straight up to London to talk to my solicitor,' I said. I started the car and drove on.

'You mustn't believe what 'ee said to you about goin' to prison,' my passenger said. 'They don't put nobody in the clink just for speedin'.'

'Are you sure of that?' I asked.

'I'm positive,' he answered. 'They can take your licence away and they can give you a whoppin' big fine, but that'll be the end of it.'

I felt tremendously relieved.

'By the way,' I said, 'why did you lie to him?'

'Who me?' he said. 'What makes you think I lied?'

'You told him you were an unemployed hod carrier. But you told *me* you were in a highly skilled trade.'

'So I am,' he said. 'But it don't pay to tell everythin' to a copper.'

'So what *do* you do?' I asked him.

'Ah,' he said slyly. 'That'd be tellin', wouldn't it?'

'Is it something you're ashamed of?'

'Ashamed?' he cried. 'Me, ashamed of my job? I'm about as proud of it as anybody could be in the entire world!'

'Then why won't you tell me?'

'You writers really is nosy parkers, aren't you?' he said. 'And you ain't goin' to be 'appy, I don't think, until you've found out exactly what the answer is?'

'I don't really care one way or the other,' I told him, lying.

He gave me a crafty little ratty look out of the sides of his eyes. 'I think you do care,' he said. 'I can see it on your face that you think I'm in some kind of a very peculiar trade and you're just achin' to know what it is.'

I didn't like the way he read my thoughts. I kept quiet and stared at the road ahead.

'You'd be right, too,' he went on. 'I *am* in a very peculiar trade. I'm in the queerest peculiar trade of 'em all.'

I waited for him to go on.

'That's why I 'as to be extra careful 'oo I'm talkin' to, you see. 'Ow am I to know, for instance, you're not another copper in plain clothes?'

'Do I look like a copper?'

'No,' he said. 'You don't. And you ain't. Any fool could tell that.'

He took from his pocket a tin of tobacco and a packet of cigarette papers and started to roll a cigarette. I was watching him out of the corner of one eye, and the speed with which he performed this rather difficult operation was incredible. The cigarette was rolled and ready in about five seconds. He ran his tongue along the edge of the paper, stuck it down and popped the cigarette between his lips. Then, as if from nowhere, a lighter appeared in his hand. The lighter flamed. The cigarette was lit. The lighter disappeared. It was altogether a remarkable performance.

'I've never seen anyone roll a cigarette as fast as that,' I said.

'Ah,' he said, taking a deep suck of smoke. 'So you noticed.'

'Of course I noticed. It was quite fantastic.'

He sat back and smiled. It pleased him very much that I had noticed how quickly he could roll a cigarette. 'You want to know what makes me able to do it?' he asked.

'Go on then.'

'It's because I've got fantastic fingers. These fingers of mine,' he said, holding up both hands high in front of him, 'are quicker and cleverer than the fingers of the best piano player in the world!'

'Are you a piano player?'

'Don't be daft,' he said. 'Do I look like a piano player?'

I glanced at his fingers. They were so beautifully shaped, so slim and long and elegant, they didn't seem to belong to the rest of him at all. They looked more like the fingers of a brain surgeon or a watchmaker.

'My job', he went on, 'is a hundred times more difficult than playin' the piano. Any twerp can learn to do that. There's titchy little kids learnin' to play the piano in almost any 'ouse you go into these days. That's right, ain't it?'

'More or less,' I said.

'Of course it's right. But there's not one person in ten million can learn to do what I do. Not one in ten million! 'Ow about that?'

'Amazing,' I said.

'You're darn right it's amazin',' he said.

'I think I know what you do,' I said. 'You do conjuring tricks. You're a conjurer.'

'Me?' he snorted. 'A conjurer? Can you picture me goin' round crummy kids' parties makin' rabbits come out of top 'ats?'

'Then you're a card player. You get people into card games and you deal yourself marvellous hands.'

'Me! A rotten card-sharper!' he cried. 'That's a miserable racket if ever there was one.'

'All right, I give up.'

I was taking the car along slowly now, at no more than forty miles an hour, to make quite sure I wasn't stopped again. We had come on to the main London–Oxford road and were running down the hill towards Denham.

Suddenly, my passenger was holding up a black leather belt in his hand. 'Ever seen this before?' he asked. The belt had a brass buckle of unusual design.

'Hey!' I said. 'That's mine, isn't it? It *is* mine! Where did you get it?'

He grinned and waved the belt gently from side to side. 'Where d'you think I got it?' he said. 'Off the top of your trousers, of course.'

I reached down and felt for my belt. It was gone.

'You mean you took it off me while we've been driving along?' I asked, flabbergasted.

He nodded, watching me all the time with those little black ratty eyes.

'That's impossible,' I said. 'You'd have had to undo the buckle and slide the whole thing out through the loops all the way round. I'd have seen you doing it. And even if I hadn't seen you, I'd have felt it.'

'Ah, but you didn't, did you?' he said, triumphant. He dropped the belt on his lap, and now all at once there was a brown shoelace dangling from his fingers. 'And what about this, then?' he exclaimed, waving the shoelace.

'What about it?' I said.

'Anyone around 'ere missin' a shoelace?' he asked, grinning.

I glanced down at my shoes. The lace of one of them was missing. 'Good grief!' I said. 'How did you do that? I never saw you bending down.'

'You never saw nothin',' he said proudly. 'You never even saw me move an inch. And you know why?'

'Yes,' I said. 'Because you've got fantastic fingers.'

'Exactly right!' he cried. 'You catch on pretty quick, don't you?' He sat back and sucked away at his home-made cigarette, blowing the smoke out in a thin stream against the windshield. He knew he had impressed me greatly with those two tricks, and this made him very happy. 'I don't want to be late,' he said. 'What time is it?'

'There's a clock in front of you,' I told him.

'I don't trust car clocks,' he said. 'What does your watch say?'

I hitched up my sleeve to look at the watch on my wrist. It wasn't there. I looked at the man. He looked back at me, grinning.

'You've taken that, too,' I said.

He held out his hand and there was my watch lying in his palm. 'Nice bit of stuff, this,' he said. 'Superior quality. Eighteen-carat gold. Easy to flog, too. It's never any trouble gettin' rid of quality goods.'

'I'd like it back, if you don't mind,' I said rather huffily.

He placed the watch carefully on the leather tray in front of him. 'I wouldn't nick anything from you, guv'nor,' he said. 'You're my pal. You're givin' me a lift.'

'I'm glad to hear it,' I said.

'All I'm doin' is answerin' your question,' he went on. 'You asked me what I did for a livin' and I'm showin' you.'

'What else have you got of mine?'

He smiled again, and now he started to take from the pocket of his jacket one thing after another that belonged to me – my driving-licence, a key-ring with four keys on it, some pound notes, a few coins, a letter from my publishers, my diary, a stubby old pencil, a cigarette-lighter, and last of all, a beautiful old sapphire ring with pearls around it belonging to my wife. I was taking the ring up to the jeweller in London because one of the pearls was missing.

'Now *there's* another lovely piece of goods,' he said, turning the ring over in his fingers. 'That's eighteenth century, if I'm not mistaken, from the reign of King George the Third.'

'You're right,' I said, impressed. 'You're absolutely right.'

He put the ring on the leather tray with the other items.

'So you're a pickpocket,' I said.

'I don't like that word,' he answered. 'It's a coarse and vulgar word. Pickpockets is coarse and vulgar people who only do easy little amateur jobs. They lift money from blind old ladies.'

'What do you call yourself, then?'

'Me? I'm a fingersmith. I'm a professional fingersmith.' He spoke the words solemnly and proudly, as though he were telling me he was the President of the Royal College of Surgeons or the Archbishop of Canterbury.

'I've never heard that word before,' I said. 'Did you invent it?'

'Of course I didn't invent it,' he replied. 'It's the name given to them who's risen to the very top of the profession. You've 'eard of a goldsmith and a silversmith, for instance. They're experts with gold and silver. I'm an expert with my fingers, so I'm a fingersmith.'

'It must be an interesting job.'

'It's a marvellous job,' he answered. 'It's lovely.'

'And that's why you go to the races?'

'Race meetings is easy meat,' he said. 'You just stand around after the race, watchin' for the lucky ones to queue up and draw their money. And when you see someone collectin' a big bundle of notes, you simply follows after 'im and 'elps yourself. But don't get me wrong, guv'nor. I never takes nothin' from a loser. Nor from poor people neither. I only go after them as can afford it, the winners and the rich.'

'That's very thoughtful of you,' I said. 'How often do you get caught?'

'Caught?' he cried, disgusted. '*Me* get caught? It's only pickpockets get caught. Fingersmiths never. Listen, I could take the false teeth out of your mouth if I wanted to and you wouldn't even catch me!'

'I don't have false teeth,' I said.

'I know you don't,' he answered. 'Otherwise I'd 'ave 'ad 'em out long ago!'

I believed him. Those long slim fingers of his seemed able to do anything.

We drove on for a while without talking.

'That policeman's going to check up on you pretty thoroughly,' I said. 'Doesn't that worry you a bit?'

'Nobody's checkin' up on me,' he said.

'Of course they are. He's got your name and address written down most carefully in his black book.

The man gave me another of his sly, ratty little smiles. 'Ah,' he said. 'So 'ee 'as. But I'll bet 'ee ain't got it all written down in 'is memory as well. I've never known a copper yet with a decent memory. Some of 'em can't even remember their own names.'

'What's memory got to do with it?' I asked. 'It's written down in his book, isn't it?'

'Yes, guv'nor, it is. But the trouble is, 'ee's lost the book. 'Ee's lost both books, the one with my name in it *and* the one with yours.'

In the long delicate fingers of his right hand, the man was holding up in triumph the two books he had taken from the policeman's pockets. 'Easiest job I ever done,' he announced proudly.

I nearly swerved the car into a milk-truck, I was so excited.

'That copper's got nothin' on either of us now,' he said.

'You're a genius!' I cried.

''Ee's got no names, no addresses, no car number, no nothin',' he said.

'You're brilliant!'

'I think you'd better pull in off this main road as soon as possible,' he said. 'Then we'd better build a little bonfire and burn these books.'

'You're a fantastic fellow,' I exclaimed.

'Thank you, guv'nor,' he said. 'It's always nice to be appreciated.'

Carousel
Carol Silcock

Mr Simpson could not believe his luck when the carousel he had seen a year ago in Germany was advertised in the 'World's Fair'. He had telephoned the number in the advert immediately and was relieved when the lady who answered the phone spoke English. The carousel had been her husband's, she explained. She felt slightly reluctant to sell it; it had seemed so special to him since it was the last set of horses he had carved, in 1991, and they really were his best. However, they were of little use to her now and so she eventually agreed a price with Mr Simpson.

Concerned in case any of the horses should be damaged, Mr Simpson arranged to travel to Munich himself, with two of his men, to collect the ride and bring it back in his lorry.

As they loaded the horses carefully into the back of the vehicle, Mr Simpson admired the craftsmanship in the carving. They were quite unique, which was why he had wanted them. He could spot the work of most of the old manufacturers, but these were different from any he had seen before. Some of the paintwork was slightly worn and would need some work, and one or two of the names were difficult to read or had letters missing, but he would re-name these after his family in the tradition of most showmen.

They drove through the night, hoping to catch one of the first trains through the Chunnel the next morning. Harry, one of the men, had driven first until they crossed the French border, where Mr Simpson took over.

It was now after two and there was little traffic on the road. Mr Simpson and Harry chatted for a while, but eventually Harry's answers became more of a grunt as he slipped slowly into sleep.

Driving along the dark, country roads, Arthur Simpson felt like he was the only person still awake on earth. There were no road lights and woods hugged either side of the road, and he suddenly felt very alone. He whistled a few songs to himself in order to stay cheery or at least awake, but he soon grew tired of this and gave up. The silence seemed greater now than before and he was aware of the acuteness of his senses as his lorry roared down the silent roads.

His mind was drifting to the jobs he would need to do on his return when he suddenly became conscious of a murmuring noise, almost like a whisper, which seemed to fill the air around him. He turned to look at the two men asleep beside him in the cab, certain that one of them must be talking in their sleep, but they both appeared to be still. He now felt too as if someone was behind him and he looked in his rear-view mirror to see if another vehicle had come along behind him without his notice. Darkness, there was only darkness all around him. He looked at the trees outside. The branches moved gently in a light breeze and with the breeze it came again, the whispering, like a sigh in the air. He could feel the clamminess of his hand on the wheel and his scalp prickled as he strained to listen . . .

'Shall I take a turn now, boss?' Joe leaned across Harry as he spoke.

'Aye, all right. I'll pull in at the next lay-by.' Arthur Simpson smiled with relief to himself, convinced that the noises he had heard were those made by Joe as he came to. Amazing, he thought, what a bit of darkness and loneliness can do to a balanced mind!

Arthur Simpson never gave the incident another thought and two days later he was building the ride up for a trial run, in the position it would occupy for the season.

As it finally came together he stood back and looked at it with pride. It was truly magnificent. The painting which needed doing did not detract from its beauty and most of it would wait until the end of the season. He started the ride up along with its organ music. Wonderful. He smiled.

The weekend was the first occasion for him to see how well his new carousel drew the crowd. Fortunately it was sunny, but there was a cool breeze which he hoped would keep people off the beach and on his rides.

The carousel proved to be a major attraction, as it had been when he saw it in Munich, riding full all day. Children tugged at their parents' sleeves, pleading to have a ride.

As the ride slowed to a halt the next punters clambered up on the horses. A little boy was helped by his father on to one of the central horses. 'Giddy up, horsey!' shouted the little boy in delight. 'What's his name, daddy?'

The boy's father tilted his head in an effort to read the now faded name. 'I don't know . . . I can't read it . . . "T" . . . "o" . . . can't read the rest. We'll call him Tonto,' he said smiling.

'Giddy up, Tonto,' shouted the little boy and he jerked the reins as he'd seen people do on television. With the movement of the reins the boy felt a quiver run through the horse, like the muscles of a real horse twitching.

Instantly, he reached for his father. 'Daddy, I don't like this horse . . . get me off.'

'Why, what's wrong?' asked his father with a smile, vaguely amused by his son's whimsiness.

'It moved, daddy. I felt it move.'

'No, the ride's not started yet son.' He emphasized it with a shake of his head and tried to reassure the little boy with a smile.

Unable to express himself any other way, the little boy's eyes filled with tears. 'I don't want to ride any more,

Daddy, and he gripped his arms tightly around his father's neck to make sure he wasn't re-mounted on the horse.

As Mr Simpson was locking the ride up later that night, he felt the wind pick up and it made him shiver involuntarily after the warm sun of the day. He looked up at the still fairground and a sudden gust of wind met him, as if someone had opened the door of a long, windy corridor. Once more, he felt uneasy, as if someone was around, watching him, from a distance, and he thought again of the lonely road in France.

He circled the ride, checking each padlock, then turned to walk to his car. As he opened the car door, he heard a muffled noise, like somebody sneezing . . . or maybe a horse snorting. He paused. Silence. He shook his head, closed the car door and drove away from the carousel.

When he drove up the next morning, Harry and Joe were both already there and were in the process of removing the shutters and padlocks. 'Morning boss,' shouted Joe, with hardly a turn of his head. 'I was just telling Harry here, there's some real weirdos around nowadays.'

'I know. Why do they all work for me though?' said Arthur with a chuckle.

'No, really,' Joe persisted. 'When I got here this morning there wasn't a soul around except this one eastern-looking fella. Had his hair tied up behind his head and what looked like a silk scarf around his neck. Really strange he was, just stood and stared for a moment and when I looked again he was gone. I'll tell you what though, you wouldn't have messed with him. He looked a really tough character.'

'Hmm,' Arthur shrugged. 'Takes all sorts to make a world, I suppose.' But he didn't like the sound of someone lurking around his rides. He was always suspicious of anyone strange.

Harry, who was walking round the ride checking the horses, stopped at one. 'This one needs some work, Mr Simpson. There's a crack, like a split between its neck and body. Can't see it's name though . . . T . . . something, A . . . maybe . . .?'

'Yeah, there's a few need some work,' Mr Simpson replied distractedly. He was still thinking about the man Joe had seen.

Harry was still looking at the same horse. 'I'll tell you something,' he said. 'I bet old Zimmerman carved this one first. If you look at it carefully, it's just that bit better than the others. Do you know, it looks more real, couldn't say why though . . . maybe the eyes. I reckon that crack needs looking at before the end of the season, Mr Simpson, it can only go worse.'

Arthur looked up at the horse which Harry was standing next to. 'Yeah. We'll have a look at the split in the next few weeks. It'll be all right for a while.' He realized how right Harry was. The line of the horse's head was slightly more graceful than the others, maybe. It could almost have been carved by a different craftsman and Zimmerman had tried to copy it, like a painter copying a masterpiece. They were good and could fool the layman, but they often lacked the subtle strokes of the master.

'We'll have to take most of the horses to the barn to be repainted,' Arthur Simpson told the men. 'Perhaps we'll do one or two of the worst between Easter and Whit, on the quiet days,' and he made a mental note to start with the horse Harry was standing next to.

People soon began to mill around as the warmth of the sun increased and Arthur's carousel once more seemed to be the major attraction. It had certainly been a good move buying these gallopers, he thought, and he congratulated himself on his decision.

The organ music blasted out and people stood around watching the horses move gently up and down, round and round, to the sound of a waltz by Strauss.

As it began to slow to a halt, a group of young lads came up, laughing, shouting and egging each other on to ride the horses, which were obviously not thrilling or daring enough for them. While they taunted each other, younger children and parents claimed their rides until there were only two horses left.

'Come on, Nick,' said the stocky, fair-haired boy, 'we'll go on,' and he grabbed his friend by his shirt sleeve and climbed up on to the ride.

Nick was taller and more slender than the other boy and he seemed less enthusiastic about the escapade. He smiled apologetically at a mother and her little girl, whom he sat next to. 'Typical,' he thought, looking at the horse. 'I get the last horse and it's broken,' and he ran his hand down the split between its neck and body.

'No more riders,' shouted the man collecting the money. 'Stand clear of the ride,' he instructed the people who were standing by.

Slowly, gently, the ride began to move as if it was a tremendous effort for the machinery which powered it, but gradually it gathered pace and went faster than Nick had realized when he'd watched it before. The breeze he felt on his face also gathered force, and he actually felt himself shiver with cold. He looked into the crowd, trying to spot his idiot friends laughing and pointing at him as he spun round and round, but instead his attention was drawn to a dark, oriental man standing further back in the crowd who, Nick felt sure, was staring at him. Each time as the ride went round faster, faster, he caught glimpses of the man until everyone else in the crowd became a blur and this man alone stood out, silent, unmoving.

Suddenly, he felt a surge of movement in the horse he was sitting on and he looked up at the rod, wondering if it was coming loose from its crank. The music of the organ became a distant sound until all that he heard was the beat, the rhythm, like the pounding of horses' hooves, hundreds of horses' hooves. He closed his eyes and held on tightly to the horse and he was no longer by the sea, but on a plain with mountains in the distance, and he felt as though he was galloping with many others, a huge force and the beat he could hear became a drumming. And above the drumming he could hear a name, someone whispering a name, 'Taikoo, Taikoo'. He could almost taste the dust from the earth in his mouth and he felt himself let out a cry, like a battle cry. His grip became tighter, but the horse began to slacken its pace until eventually it came to a halt and he opened his eyes.

Jason was standing next to him with a wide grin on his face. 'What's the matter? Frightened of falling off, little boy?' He laughed mockingly and Nick realized he still had both hands clasped tightly around the horse's neck. He blushed, feeling foolish in front of his friends. 'Something happened . . .' he began, but realizing how fantastic his explanation might sound, he simply said, 'It felt like it was breaking away from its supports.'

'Yeah, looks all right to me,' and Jason winked at him. But something had happened, Nick was sure. He touched the horse as they moved to leave the platform in an effort to convince himself it was no more than a piece of wood. It was completely solid.

He looked around at the faces in the crowd, but the oriental man was no longer there. Maybe he was coming down with a virus, Nick thought, maybe he had mistaken what he saw, maybe . . .

Arthur Simpson watched as the young lads walked away from the ride, still laughing and joking, and he noticed the taller, slender boy seemed to be the target of the others' jokes for a while. He smiled, recollecting his own youthful escapades.

He went to change the music for the organ and as he was feeding the paper music into the machine, he wondered if Mrs Zimmerman might have any more music for it. He would call her that evening to find out.

'Well, Mr Simpson, you must have read my mind,' Mrs Zimmerman declared, later that evening. 'I was only thinking of you last night when I was going through some boxes of my husband's, and yes, there were two large ones with organ music in them. You may as well have them. After all, they belong with the carousel.'

Arthur Simpson offered her a fair price and agreed to send her a cheque the following morning.

'How is the carousel?' asked Mrs Zimmerman.

'It's a beauty,' replied Arthur. 'We've had it running the last few days and it looks really well. Do you know, Mrs Zimmerman, I only thought the other day how well carved it is, but there's one horse in particular whose workmanship is very special. Your husband really was a master craftsman.'

'I know which horse you mean, Mr Simpson. It's Taikoo isn't it? You must have a keen eye. That was the first horse which Mr Zimmerman carved for that carousel. He started it after a trip to China, said he'd copied it from the figures he saw belonging to some emperor's tomb around Xi'an. He always loved old artefacts and antiques, you know, anything which he thought was beautiful. He collected many things like that you know, but was never one for displaying it all. Most of it was simply packed away, somewhere or other.'

'Well, he certainly had an eye for beauty, I can vouch for that. When we've repainted the carousel, at the end of the season, and restored it to its former glory, you should come across to England and see it, have a holiday and we'll show you around.'

'That would be lovely,' said the old lady. 'You're very kind. I'll parcel your music up and send it to you tomorrow, Mr Simpson. Goodbye . . . and thank you.'

'Goodbye, Mrs Zimmerman.'

That night, as Arthur Simpson got ready for bed, he opened his window and looked out towards the sea. The warmth of the day had left the house feeling airless, but now he could feel a drizzle in the air and a breeze was beginning to pick up. Nevertheless, as he climbed into bed, he still felt sticky and lay on top of the sheets in an attempt to stay cool. It was a while before he drifted into a restless sleep.

He dreamt of a dark stranger who moved silently towards the carousel. There was no one else around. He seemed to be talking to one of the horses, whispering its name, 'Taikoo, Taikoo . . .' and as he climbed on to the horse they were both transported to a different land. They were riding with many others, soldiers going into battle, the noise, the heat and the screams made Arthur recoil, but he was being propelled forward. He could not stop himself. He watched in horror at the twisted faces and contorted shapes as men and horses lay dying around him. Awful scenes and the smell of fear. He could see mountains in the distance and wished he too was there and not on that blood-washed plain. He saw death and suddenly found himself in a cold, dark place and realized with terror that it was a tomb. He was buried alive and faintly, in the darkness, he could see the shape of a horse's head . . .

He came to, gasping for air, with droplets of sweat all over his face. He sat up quickly to make sure where he was. The morning sun was just beginning to light up the wall in his bedroom and he lay back, exhausted.

When he finally arrived at work that morning he had shaken off the terrors of the night and the sweet scents in the air made him feel fresh and alive. He saw Harry walking towards him and smiled, knowing that there was going to be some trivial problem for him to sort out.

'Well, what is it, Harry?'

'There's a Chinese man, by the carousel, wants to speak to you.'

Captain Murderer
Charles Dickens

If we all knew our own minds (in a more enlarged sense than the popular acceptation of that phrase), I suspect we should find our nurses responsible for most of the dark corners we are forced to go back to, against our wills.

The first diabolical character who intruded himself on my peaceful youth was a certain Captain Murderer. This wretch must have been an offshoot of the Blue Beard family, but I had no suspicion of the **consanguinity** in those times. His warning name would seem to have awakened no general prejudice against him, for he was admitted into the best society and possessed immense wealth. Captain Murderer's mission was matrimony, and the gratification of a cannibal appetite with tender brides. On his marriage morning, he always caused both sides of the way to church to be planted with curious flowers; and when his bride said, 'Dear Captain Murderer, I never saw flowers like these before: what are they called?' he answered, 'They are called Garnish for house-lamb,' and laughed at his ferocious practical joke in a horrid manner, disquieting the minds of the noble bridal company, with a very sharp show of teeth, then displayed for the first time. He made love in a coach and six, and married in a coach and twelve, and all his horses were milk-white horses with one red spot on the back which he caused to be hidden by the harness. For, the spot *would* come there, though every horse was milk-white when Captain Murderer bought him. And the spot was young bride's blood. (*To this terrific point I am indebted for my first personal*

---

consanguinity: blood relationship

experience of a shudder and cold beads on the forehead.) When Captain Murderer had made an end of feasting and revelry, and had dismissed the noble guests, and was alone with his wife on the day month after their marriage, it was his whimsical custom to produce a golden rolling-pin and a silver pie-board. Now, there was this special feature in the Captain's courtships, that he always asked if the young lady could make pie-crust; and if she couldn't by nature or education, she was taught. Well. When the bride saw Captain Murderer produce the golden rolling-pin and silver pie-board, she remembered this, and turned up her laced-silk sleeves to make a pie. The Captain brought out a silver pie-dish of immense capacity, and the Captain brought out flour and butter and eggs and all things needful, except the inside of the pie; of materials for the staple of the pie itself, the Captain brought out none. Then said the lovely bride, 'Dear Captain Murderer, what pie is this to be?' He replied, 'A meat pie.' Then said the lovely bride, 'Dear Captain Murderer, I see no meat.' The Captain humorously retorted, 'Look in the glass.' She looked in the glass, but still she saw no meat, and then the Captain roared with laughter, and suddenly frowning and drawing his sword, bade her roll out the crust. So she rolled out the crust, dropping large tears upon it all the time because he was so cross, and when she had lined the dish with crust and had cut the crust all ready to fit the top, the Captain called out, '*I* see the meat in the glass!' And the bride looked up at the glass, just in time to see the Captain cutting her head off; and he chopped her in pieces, and peppered her, and salted her, and put her in the pie, and sent it to the baker's, and ate it all, and picked the bones.

Captain Murderer went on in this way, prospering exceedingly, until he came to choose a bride from two twin sisters, and at first didn't know which to choose. For, though one was fair and the other dark, they were both equally beautiful. But the fair twin loved him, and the dark twin hated him, so he chose the fair one. The dark twin would have prevented the marriage if she could, but she couldn't; however, on the night before it, much suspecting Captain Murderer, she stole out and climbed his garden wall, and looked in at his window through a chink in the shutter, and saw him having his teeth filed sharp. Next day she listened all day, and heard him make his joke about the house-lamb. And that day month, he had the paste rolled out, and cut the fair twin's head off, and chopped her in pieces, and peppered her, and salted her, and put her in the pie, and sent it to the baker's, and ate it all, and picked the bones.

Now, the dark twin had had her suspicions much increased by the filing of the Captain's teeth, and again by the house-lamb joke. Putting all things together when he gave out that her sister was dead, she divined the truth, and determined to be revenged. So, she went up to Captain Murderer's house, and knocked at the knocker and pulled at the bell, and when the Captain came to the door, said: 'Dear Captain Murderer, marry me next for I always loved you and was jealous of my sister.' The Captain took it as a compliment, and made a polite answer, and the marriage was quickly arranged. On the night before it, the bride again climbed to his window, and again saw him having his teeth filed sharp. At this sight she laughed such a terrible laugh at the chink in the shutter, that the Captain's blood curdled, and he said: 'I hope nothing has disagreed with me!' At that, she laughed again, a still more terrible laugh, and the shutter was opened and search made, but she was nimbly gone, and there was no one. Next day they went to church in a coach and twelve, and were married. And that day month, she rolled the pie-crust out, and Captain Murderer cut her head off, and chopped her in pieces, and peppered her, and salted her, and put her in the pie, and sent it to the baker's, and ate it all, and picked the bones.

But before she began to roll out the paste she had taken a deadly poison of a most awful character, distilled from toads' eyes and spiders' knees; and Captain Murderer had hardly picked her last bone, when he began to swell, and to turn blue, and to be all over spots, and to scream. And he went on swelling and turning bluer, and being more all over spots and screaming, until he reached from floor to ceiling and from wall to wall; and then, at one o'clock in the morning, he blew up with a loud explosion. At the sound of it, all the milk-white horses in the stables broke their halters and went mad, and then they galloped over everybody in Captain Murderer's house (beginning with the family blacksmith who had filed his teeth) until the whole were dead, and then they galloped away.

The Case for the Defence
Graham Greene

It was the strangest murder trial I ever attended. They named it the Peckham murder in the headlines, though Northwood Street, where the old woman was found battered to death, was not strictly speaking in Peckham. This was not one of those cases of **circumstantial evidence** in which you feel the jurymen's anxiety – because mistakes *have* been made – like domes of silence muting the court. No, this murderer was all but found with the body: no one present when the **Crown counsel** outlined his case believed that the man in the dock stood any chance at all.

He was a heavy stout man with bulging bloodshot eyes. All his muscles seemed to be in his thighs. Yes, an ugly customer, one you wouldn't forget in a hurry – and that was an important point because the Crown proposed to call four witnesses who hadn't forgotten him, who had seen him hurrying away from the little red villa in Northwood Street. The clock had just struck two in the morning.

Mrs Salmon in 15 Northwood Street had been unable to sleep; she heard a door click shut and thought it was her own gate. So she went to the window and saw Adams (that was his name) on the steps of Mrs Parker's house. He had just come out and he was wearing gloves. He had a hammer in his hand and she saw him drop it into the

---

circumstantial evidence: evidence of the circumstances without the person actually having been witnessed
Crown counsel: the barrister or lawyer presenting the case against the accused

laurel bushes by the front gate. But before he moved away, he had looked up – at her window. The fatal instinct that tells a man when he is watched exposed him in the light of a street-lamp to her gaze – his eyes suffused with horrifying and brutal fear, like an animal's when you raise a whip. I talked afterwards to Mrs Salmon, who naturally after the astonishing verdict went in fear herself. As I imagine did all the witnesses – Henry MacDougall, who had been driving home from Benfleet late and nearly ran Adams down at the corner of Northwood Street. Adams was walking in the middle of the road looking dazed. And old Mr Wheeler, who lived next door to Mrs Parker at No. 12, and was wakened by a noise – like a chair falling – through the thin-as-paper villa wall, and got up and looked out of the window, just as Mrs Salmon had done, saw Adams's back and, as he turned, those bulging eyes. In Laurel Avenue he had been seen by yet another witness – his luck was badly out; he might as well have committed the crime in broad daylight.

'I understand,' counsel said, 'that the defence proposes to plead mistaken identity. Adams's wife will tell you that he was with her at two in the morning on February 14, but after you have heard the witnesses for the Crown and examined carefully the features of the prisoner, I do not think you will be prepared to admit the possibility of a mistake.'

It was all over, you would have said, but the hanging.

After the formal evidence had been given by the policeman who had found the body and the surgeon who had examined it, Mrs Salmon was called. She was the ideal witness, with her slight Scotch accent and her expression of honesty, care and kindness.

The counsel for the Crown brought the story gently out. She spoke very firmly. There was no malice in her, and no sense of importance at standing there in the

Central Criminal Court with a judge in scarlet hanging on her words and the reporters writing them down. Yes, she said, and then she had gone downstairs and rung up the police station.

'And do you see the man here in court?'

She looked straight at the big man in the dock, who stared hard at her with his pekingese eyes without emotion.

'Yes,' she said, 'there he is.'

'You are quite certain?'

She said simply, 'I couldn't be mistaken, sir.'

It was all as easy as that.

'Thank you, Mrs Salmon.'

Counsel for the defence rose to cross-examine. If you had reported as many murder trials as I have, you would have known beforehand what line he would take. And I was right, up to a point.

'Now, Mrs Salmon, you must remember that a man's life may depend on your evidence.'

'I do remember it, sir.'

'Is your eyesight good?'

'I have never had to wear spectacles, sir.'

'You are a woman of fifty-five?'

'Fifty-six, sir.'

'And the man you saw was on the other side of the road?'

'Yes, sir.'

'And it was two o'clock in the morning. You must have remarkable eyes, Mrs Salmon?'

'No, sir. There was moonlight, and when the man looked up, he had the lamplight on his face.'

'And you have no doubt whatever that the man you saw is the prisoner?'

I couldn't make out what he was at. He couldn't have expected any other answer than the one he got.

'None whatever, sir. It isn't a face one forgets.'

Counsel took a look round the court for a moment. Then he said, 'Do you mind, Mrs Salmon, examining again the people in court? No, not the prisoner. Stand up, please, Mr Adams,' and there at the back of the court with thick stout body and muscular legs and a pair of bulging eyes, was the exact image of the man in the dock. He was even dressed the same – tight blue suit and striped tie.

'Now think very carefully, Mrs Salmon. Can you still swear that the man you saw drop the hammer in Mrs Parker's garden was the prisoner – and not this man who is his twin brother?'

Of course she couldn't. She looked from one to the other and didn't say a word.

There the big brute sat in the dock with his legs crossed and there he stood too at the back of the court and they both stared at Mrs Salmon. She shook her head.

What we saw then was the end of the case. There wasn't a witness prepared to swear that it was the prisoner he'd seen. And the brother? He had his alibi too; he was with his wife.

And so the man was acquitted for lack of evidence. But whether – if he did the murder and not his brother – he was punished or not, I don't know. That extraordinary day had an extraordinary end. I followed Mrs Salmon out of court and we got wedged in the crowd who were waiting, of course, for the twins. The police tried to draw the crowd away, but all they could do was keep the roadway clear for traffic. I learned later that they tried to get the twins to leave by a back way, but they wouldn't. One of them – no one knew which – said, 'I've been acquitted, haven't I?' and they walked bang out of the front entrance. Then it happened. I don't know how, though I was only six feet away. The crowd moved and somehow one of the twins got pushed on the road right in front of a bus.

He gave a squeal like a rabbit and that was all; he was dead, his skull smashed just as Mrs Parker's had been. Divine vengeance? I wish I knew. There was the other Adams getting on his feet from beside the body and looking straight over at Mrs Salmon. He was crying, but whether he was the murderer or the innocent man nobody will ever be able to tell. But if you were Mrs Salmon, could you sleep at night?

Crime and Mystery: Activities

Reading crime and mystery stories

1 In *The Hitch-hiker*, both the narrator and the hitch-hiker commit crimes, but we feel sympathetic towards them. Write an explanation of how Roald Dahl makes us sympathize with the criminals, using examples from the text to support your comments. Think about:

- the nature of the crimes committed
- the use of the first person
- the narrator's excitement about his car
- the way the hitch-hiker explains his 'trade'
- the language and actions of the policeman
- the hitch-hiker's choice of victim.

2 a) Look at *Carousel*. Make a list of all the clues the writer gives that the horse is unusual. For example, 'he suddenly became conscious of a murmuring noise . . .'

   b) The mystery of the horse is left unsolved. In groups, discuss what might be an explanation for the events, using your list from 2a) to help you.

3 a) Although *Captain Murderer* is quite horrific, it has been included in the Crime and Mystery section of this book. Answer the following questions before coming to a decision about whether this is the best classification for the story.

   - What is the crime in the story?
   - Are there any mysterious elements to the story that are unexplained?

- What clues are given to hint that Captain Murderer will be punished?
- How is he punished?
- Do you find the ending satisfactory?

When you have thought about these questions, discuss with a partner whether this story should have been included in this section of the book.

b) Look at *Captain Murderer* and *The Case for the Defence*. What are the similarities and differences between the two? Think about:

- the nature of the crime
- whether the criminal is punished by society
- whether the criminal is punished at all and, if so, by whom
- the other characters in the story – how they contribute to the punishment and how they put themselves in danger
- the type of narrator and his/her relationship to the action
- any other parallels that you can think of.

4 a) Re-read *The Case for the Defence*. Fill in the table below, making a list of all the evidence against Mr Adams up to the point at which his brother appears.

Evidence	Example from the text
• where and when he was seen	on the steps of Mrs Parker's house in Northwood Street
• who saw him	
• what he was wearing and carrying	
• his actions and attitude	

b) What do you think the narrator means by his final question: 'But if you were Mrs Salmon, could you sleep at night?'

c) Did you expect the story to end as it did? Do you find this a satisfactory ending? Why, or why not?

Original writing

1 a) Look at the part of *The Hitch-hiker* from the point where the policeman stops the narrator to the point where he leaves again. Rewrite this passage so that the reader feels sympathetic to the policeman – not to the two men in the car. You will need to change the speech and actions of all three characters to:

- emphasize the serious nature of the crimes
- make the narrator and the hitch-hiker seem less reasonable and the policeman seem more so
- show the bad side of the hitch-hiker's character.

b) If your version was part of the real story, would you need to change the ending?

2 Use your notes from 2a) and your discussion from 2b) to write another two paragraphs to go at the end of *Carousel*. In your paragraphs you should offer an explanation of events and of the Chinaman so that everything is clear to the reader.

3 In *Captain Murderer*, the Captain's last wife kills herself in order to avenge her sister's death. Imagine that she writes a note to her family before her death, explaining her actions. Write the note, including details of:

- what she suspected about the Captain and why
- why she married him.

- why she is allowing herself to be killed
- how she feels about her actions.

4 Write your own courtroom story of about 350 words. Follow the same structure as *A Case for the Defence*. For example:
  - Think of a crime that has been committed and a criminal who looks obviously guilty.
  - Describe the criminal and outline all the evidence against him/her.
  - Reveal an unknown factor that either throws doubt on the guilt of the criminal or proves his/her innocence.
  - Think of a final twist that will surprise your reader at the end.

Heinemann
New Windmills

Founding Editors: Anne and Ian Serraillier

Chinua Achebe Things Fall Apart
David Almond Skellig
Maya Angelou I Know Why the Caged Bird Sings
Margaret Atwood The Handmaid's Tale
Jane Austen Pride and Prejudice
J G Ballard Empire of the Sun
Stan Barstow Joby; A Kind of Loving
Nina Bawden Carrie's War; Devil by the Sea; Kept in the Dark; The Finding; Humbug
Lesley Beake A Cageful of Butterflies
Malorie Blackman Tell Me No Lies; Words Last Forever
Martin Booth Music on the Bamboo Radio
Ray Bradbury The Golden Apples of the Sun; The Illustrated Man
Betsy Byars The Midnight Fox; The Pinballs; The Not-Just-Anybody Family; The Eighteenth Emergency
Victor Canning The Runaways
Jane Leslie Conly Racso and the Rats of NIMH
Robert Cormier We All Fall Down
Roald Dahl Danny, The Champion of the World; The Wonderful Story of Henry Sugar; George's Marvellous Medicine; The BFG; The Witches; Boy; Going Solo; Matilda; My Year
Anita Desai The Village by the Sea
Charles Dickens A Christmas Carol; Great Expectations; Hard Times; Oliver Twist; A Charles Dickens Selection
Peter Dickinson Merlin Dreams
Berlie Doherty Granny was a Buffer Girl; Street Child
Roddy Doyle Paddy Clarke Ha Ha Ha
Anne Fine The Granny Project
Jamila Gavin The Wheel of Surya
Graham Greene The Third Man and The Fallen Idol; Brighton Rock
Thomas Hardy The Withered Arm and Other Wessex Tales
L P Hartley The Go-Between
Ernest Hemmingway The Old Man and the Sea; A Farewell to Arms
Frances Mary Hendry Chandra
Barry Hines A Kestrel For A Knave
Nigel Hinton Getting Free; Buddy; Buddy's Song; Out of the Darkness
Anne Holm I Am David

Janni Howker Badger on the Barge; The Nature of the Beast; Martin Farrell

Pete Johnson The Protectors

Jennifer Johnston Shadows on Our Skin

Geraldine Kaye Comfort Herself

Daniel Keyes Flowers for Algernon

Clive King Me and My Million

Dick King-Smith The Sheep-Pig

Elizabeth Laird Red Sky in the Morning; Kiss the Dust

D H Lawrence The Fox and The Virgin and the Gypsy; Selected Tales

George Layton The Swap

Harper Lee To Kill a Mockingbird

Julius Lester Basketball Game

C Day Lewis The Otterbury Incident

Joan Lingard Across the Barricades; The File on Fraulein Berg

Penelope Lively The Ghost of Thomas Kempe

Jack London The Call of the Wild; White Fang

Bernard MacLaverty Cal; The Best of Bernard Mac Laverty

Margaret Mahy The Haunting

Anthony Masters Wicked

James Vance Marshall Walkabout

Ian McEwan The Daydreamer; A Child in Time

Pat Moon The Spying Game

Michael Morpurgo My Friend Walter; The Wreck of the Zanzibar; The War of Jenkins' Ear; Why the Whales Came; Arthur, High King of Britain

Beverley Naidoo No Turning Back

Bill Naughton The Goalkeeper's Revenge

New Windmill A Charles Dickens Selection

New Windmill Book of Classic Short Stories

New Windmill Book of Fiction and Non-fiction: Taking Off!

New Windmill Book of Haunting Tales

New Windmill Book of Humorous Stories: Don't Make Me Laugh

New Windmill Book of Nineteenth Century Short Stories

New Windmill Book of Non-fiction: Get Real!

New Windmill Book of Non-fiction: Real Lives, Real Times

New Windmill Book of Scottish Short Stories

New Windmill Book of Short Stories: Fast and Curious

New Windmill Book of Short Stories: Tales with a Twist

How many have you read?